How a
PLAYER
Got PLAYED

BASED ON MY TRUE STORY

THE-LOU

ASPIRE
PUBLISHING HUB LLC.

ISBN
978-1-962611-52-7 (Paperback)
978-1-962611-53-4 (eBook)

How a
PLAYER
Got PLAYED

BASED ON MY TRUE STORY

Table of Contents

Introduction

I would like to start off by saying this story is based on what happened to me in this relationship. Every story has a beginning, middle and ending. I didn't know Ny as I will call her in this story in the early years of her life, but based on how bad she treated me, I think she would have been this type of person.

The character Will-Die is not my brother as I portray him in this story but a combination of two of my cousins. One of them had to be the smartest man I ever met and the other one was known not to be a killer! I did this because I don't want to confuse the reader with too many characters. From when I introduce myself into the story, from that point on are true accounts of happenings. I hope that anyone reading this story can learn a lot about the people you are dealing with and recognize the lies they tell.

Please keep this in mind, people are not playing games, they are just flat out lying to you. Games have rules, and there are no rules when it comes to love and life. In other words, anything goes, and name me one game you can play where you can make up the rules as you go along. No such thing; is it?! But when you find yourself in a relationship and the person, you're with is saying one thing and doing something else; I hope you don't look at it like they are playing games; they are just flat out lying to you. Remember if you have to think twice; it's not right and if you think something is wrong, well it sure in hell is.

Most people get caught up in those old clichés like, you can't judge a book by its cover and that is the exception, NOT THE RULE! That cliché is one of the dumbest things I ever heard. First, how do you know it's a book? By looking at the cover, because it is the cover that tells you what's inside. Just like when you were in school, when it was time to go to history class how did you know what book to grab? Did you open each book you had; no, you looked at the cover, right! How would you have felt if you went to history class and opened the book that said history on the cover but when opened it, it was math; you would think something was wrong. Wouldn't you? But so many people believe that you can't judge the book by its cover that they forget about the power of the subconscious mind. Without realizing it, they start making excuses based on that cliché without taking time to see the situation for what it really is. As far as I am concerned, if it looks like a duck, if it quacks like a duck and if it walks like a duck, it sure in the hell ain't no fucking ELEPHANT now is it! But some people will still say, well, you just never know, you can't judge a book by its cover. It could be an Elephant. Yes, some people are just that damn dumb and then they wonder how come they keep getting taken advantage of. Always remember 9 times out of 10; what you see is what you get.

Well, I hope my story will help some of you know the difference of when someone is for you or when they just don't give a damn about you. The type of player I am is not found in the dictionary and my way of life and education can't be taught at any college or state university. The only thing in the dictionary that is close to being the type of player I am a good actor. I would make my stories believable and show the right emotion and I would tell a little bit of the truth and follow it with a big lie. For example, I would tell my woman that I am hanging out with the boys and I would go by her job or wherever she was at and would have one of them of them with me. She would see me with my friend and it's already in her mind I am with the boys. I would drop him off and go see the lady I wanted to be with, and I never let my friend know what I was doing, because some of them are your biggest back stabbers. Some guys wonder how their woman knows what they are doing and it's because their friend told on them, hoping he could get his woman.

I always tried to keep as many people out of my business as possible but by St. Louis being a town where you can go wherever you want. What I mean by that, some cities are separated by gang lines. If you are not from that part of town, then you better not have your ass over there, but in St. Louis, we go wherever we want. I could be on the north side, south side, west side, East St. Louis and no matter where I was at, I would see someone I know, and people will talk. Over a period of time, I had developed a reputation of having a lot of fine big booty women. They say there are 12 women to every man and at one time in my life, I had my 12 and somebody else's. LOL. My problem wasn't getting a woman, it was keeping them.

At my best, I would say I had about 6 women I was seeing at one time. It would be days that I would have sex with 3 or 4 different women on the same day. I would have what I called my number one. She was the one I lied to the most. The other women, I would say that I am single, and I do date just to keep them interested and thinking that something may become of our relationship when I had no intentions on being one on one with any of them. Eventually they will get tired of me and go on about their business. But it seems like when one would fall off, I picked another one up. I never thought of myself as a player, but it was everyone else I knew that told me I was one, especially the women. They would get mad at me and say, you ain't no good, you ain't nothing but a got damn player. Guys would come up to me and tell their partners they were with and say, this is Luther and this brother is a true player. Every woman I ever seen him with was fine as hell. If you don't know what you are, just listen to the people you know like your friends, family, co-workers and they will tell you. Judging by their definition of a player, I guess I would be considered one.

One guy came up to me and said "How do you get all these women and how are you able to keep up with them, without them finding out about each other? I told him what I would do. Every woman that I considered to be my number one, I kept a notebook on the lies I told. The dates and times, so when it ever came back up, I could remember what I said, because one thing about lies, you will forget. She could bring something up from a month ago and if I couldn't remember, I would tell her to hold on while I am looking at my notes or if she was with me, I would change the subject until I could get home and look at my notes. But one of the most important things is that I try to keep everything the same. I would buy bed sheets that look just alike so she wouldn't know when I was changing them or not. I always spray Fabreeze on my pillows and bed sheets so that it will always smell the same. Every time a woman would get out of my car or out of my bed, I would look for anything she would have left behind, like those cheap ass costume jewelry they wear on purpose just to leave it in your bed or your car. That shit had got me is so much trouble that I would start talking about how I hate a cheap looking ass woman, so they would stop wearing it because I knew that their intention was leaving it someplace where I wouldn't find it, but my woman would. Women will use your bathroom to brush or comb their hair and either throw the hair

3

away in the trash, throw it on the floor or leave the comb or brush on your dresser or in the bathroom with their hair still in it. I never let a woman get in my car or bed with all that glitter on or wearing any clothing that sheds like those cheap ass sequin sweaters and shirts they wear. That shit will go everywhere and get stuck on your car seats, your couch, in your carpet and most importantly, it gets stuck on you and your clothing and how are you going to explain to the next woman that you haven't been with another woman. You know it's all going to be the same color and it's all over you and your car and your house? All that does is let the next woman know you have been with another woman. And by the way, if she is my number one, she ain't wearing any of that shit around me. But after all, she may not stay my number one and I could be looking to replace her, and I don't want too much evidence that another woman has been hanging around.

Now I am going to get to the real point. Most people have these four things in common and if you can tap into one of these four things I am talking about, chances are you could get the person you're dealing with right where you want them. But they must LIKE you in order for it to work. I tell guys all the time, you don't choose the woman; she chooses you. The average woman knows right then and there when she meets a man whether or not if she is going to deal with him. Most guys mess it up for themselves because they keep on talking when they meet a woman, when they should exchange information and keep it moving. Without realizing it, they talk so much that they just turn the woman off and the only thing the man just did was talk himself right out of the pussy and now he just messed up one of the four things he could tap into that he would need to help control that woman.

Number one is SELF. Everyone wants the best for themselves, and some don't care how they get it. But the key is to make them feel good about themselves, find out what their insecurities are and turn them into something positive, the chances are they will love you for it and it will make them feel like you are good for them; that you are on their side, when you're not.

Number two is WHAT WE LIKE. Find out what they like to do and do it with them and if you don't like it, act like you do. (women do it all the time with men in the bedroom if they are getting some money out of them). Now they are starting to think there is something in common. Now it's time to start building a relationship and a certain amount of trust comes with that. And once they start believing in you, the sky could be the limit, if you don't get too careless and stupid.

Number three is SECURITY. This is really important to a woman. What helped me be a player is that I look like I have it going on. I have my own place, car, job and dress well but sometimes wouldn't have fifty cent in my pocket. But because I look like I could provide security, a lot of women would come out of their pockets to prove to me, that they are the one for me. I would spend a little and get a lot in return. For example, I would meet a woman, we will go out and I would pay for everything on our first couple of dates, I would never brag on myself, nor would I talk about sex, getting high or other women unless they brought it up. Now their thinking, here is a good man; and they will call and say something like would you want to go to this concert, party, etc. I would tell them, I would love to, but I am broke, I just paid my rent and bills plus my car insurance is due. They would say, don't worry about it, I got it. And as time went on as we grew closer the next thing I know, I am getting gifts that I didn't ask for, money put into my hands. Sometimes I would hint around about something I wanted and the next thing I knew, I got it.

But the most important thing out of the 4 is the sex; because, if none of these women liked me in the bedroom, they sure as hell ain't going to spend their time or money on me. So, Number 4 is SEX. Now this is what gets everyone hooked, especially a man. I am going to break it down like this. A woman is more concerned with how a man is living and if he is good in bed, she doesn't give a damn what he looks like. If a man can provide and be good in bed, that would be enough for the average woman. But a man is different; he really isn't concerned about security from a woman. A man is truly turned on by sight. This lets you know that I am right about what I am saying. A woman says to one of her girlfriends, I got this guy I want you to meet and the first thing the woman is going to ask is, what does he do for a living? If a man says to one of his friends, I have this woman I want you to meet, the first thing the man is going to say is, what does she look like? If a man finds a woman that truly turns him on, she is really good in bed and now he just lost his mind. Every woman doesn't turn a man on to that degree and a lot of women are not that good in bed, but when a man finds those two things in a woman, he would do things that he ordinarily wouldn't do, like spend all of his money on her, leave his wife and kids, and if it came down to it, Yes, he would even kill somebody for her.

But I will be the first to admit that most of the women I have had left me, not me leaving them because I had no money to give them. I can't count how many women I have had over the years, that told me "Luther you are a nice guy and fun and good in bed but I need a man that's going to put some money in my pocket and you're not doing it, so I have to go; and see you around. Remember, women are looking for security and men think that the woman is in love with him and don't realize she's there because she is being taken care of, but how many times have a man lost his job and shortly after that, he loses his woman, it happens a lot more than people think.

I tell every man I know that most women are the real PLAYERS out here and they have two types of men in their lives; they have their lover and they have their provider. When you meet her, you better make up in your mind which one of them you are going to be, because if you don't it could make the difference whether you end up in the Penitentiary or Cemetery. Just about every man I know has been over a woman's house at one time in his life or another and another man shows up who she is dealing with. Most of the time, I will call this man the provider, because he thinks that he is paying for everything that he has the right to show up whenever he pleases even if he doesn't live there. Now he either kicks the door down or he has a key, but when he gets inside and see another man there, now we have a big fight going on and it's a chance that one of them will end up dead and the other one is going to jail. Now most men are so aggressive that they will not take time to think about what they are doing, and the woman has already plan this out, hoping this situation would happen.

Now a lot of guys out here think that they are players. Take the ones that don't have much, but they come across a woman that's got it going on and she takes an interest in him. They develop a relationship and he's thinking I got this super fine woman and she is spending money on me and fucking me good and don't realize he may be getting set up. The average super fine woman ain't going to be spending a whole lot of money on a man unless she getting it from another man. Now remember a woman has her lover and has her provider. But when she meets a man that has it all (he is a good lover and provider) that means the other two have to go. So what does she do? She would let them meet and will have them both so mad at each other that they will be ready to fight at first sight. This woman tells her lover that her ex has been giving her problems and he won't leave her alone; he is going to hurt me badly. Now the lover tells her, don't worry about it, baby, I got your back, when he comes over, I will be ready for him. Now the woman tells her provider that I had this old boyfriend and he found out where I lived, and he's been coming over and he won't leave me alone. The provider says, ok, I will take care of that; so, one day the provider is over the woman's place and she picks up the phone and calls the lover and says he is over here. The lover rushes over to her. When the lover arrives, she turns to the provider instigating, indicating it is him. provider pulls out his gun and as soon as she opens the door, the lover see's the provider with his gun already out and he reaches for his and they have a shootout and the provider kills the lover. When the police come, the woman tells the story of the provider being a jealous boyfriend and shot her friend. Now she just got rid of both of them. That's literally killing two birds with one stone. The lover is dead and the provider is going to the Penitentiary (death row).

And the moral to this story as I found out and I will tell any man that thinks he is a player … DON'T EVER UNDERESTIMATE THE POWER OF THE PUSSY.

You read it here 1st! I'am going to change the informal definition of a player in the dictionary- Their definition of a player is "A confident, successful man with many sexual partners. They are WRONG! it should be a confident successful person - because women are the biggest players and some of them have many sexual partners - Maury Povick and paternity court has proven this so many times plus a very beautiful woman with a great body doesn't gave to be successful. She may not have a dime or any income but she could get a very successful man to leave his wife and kids for her every day some man somewhere has fallen for a broke beautiful woman with a great body and a smile and then she kicks him to the curb when she done playing him happens everyday!!

PLEASE EMAIL THEM

SUPPORT @.MERRIAMWEBSTER. FRESHDESK.
COM

I

 he year is 1980 in New York, New York. There is a young black woman walking down the street, and she is a very pretty woman with a body that every man would die for. But she is not a woman, but a 15-year-old girl.

A young boy pulls up in his car and asks her, "What's your name?"

"Nigeria," she answered.

"Hi! How are you doing?" The boy said. "My name is Lorenzo, and I think you're a really fine woman!" He continued. "And I would love to see you sometime?" The man said after a long pause.

"That would be okay, but I'm just 15!" Nigeria replied. "What about you?" She asked the man out of curiosity.

"Me? I'm 17." Lorenzo replied, gazing at her.

"Um... But you look older than that?" Nigeria replied, staring him back in disbelief. After a pause, she said, "Is that your car?"

"No! Not exactly! It's my father's!" Lorenzo replied. "And yeah! I am 17 years old." He continued, affirming his age.

"Well! Okay! So, here's my number, and when you call, just ask for Ni." Nigeria replied, handing her number to him.

Lorenzo nods his head and pulls off. Ny starts walking down the street; men are passing by, blowing their horns. As she walked, one of the men suddenly stopped to get her attention and got hit from behind.

"Damn, baby! Did you see what you made me just do? I just got my car hit trying to holler at you." The man said to Ni. He almost hit his car trying to save her from a mishap. Ny was relieved, but before Ny could say anything, the man driving the other car jumped out, mad as hell.

"What in the fuck is wrong with you, mother fucker? Don't you know you could get somebody killed stopping like that for no reason?" The other man yelled in the middle of the road.

"Hey brother, I am sorry, but I just had to stop to save this lady walking in the middle of the road." The man whose car got hit said in an apologetic tone.

"How old are you, man?? 35, maybe 40!" He yelled at the man. He sounded quite frustrated at the moment.

"I'm 38," The man who saved the girl answered, trying to keep himself calm.

"Take a good look, man, because that fine woman could not be no more than 15 or 16 years old, and now you just mess up both of our cars chasing something at 38 you have no damn business with." The other man said. He was annoyed as his car was damaged.

The man then looked at Ny and realized the other man was right.

Embarrassed by the mess he created unintentionally, the man handed over a car to him and said, "Here's my insurance card and my number. I will take care of this. Don't worry!"

The other man took the card and turned around to speak to Ni, "Young lady! Please be careful. There are a whole lot of dirty old men out here. That doesn't mean you are no good. Hope you get my point!"

Ny shakes her head as if she understands and walks away with a big smile on her face.

"How come I get the feeling that she is not going to be the one who has to be careful, but some of them fellas that she will run into later on in life."

The man said to himself as he stood there on the road all by himself.

"I will have to agree with you. Did you notice her smiling? She enjoys seeing two men wreck their cars because one of them was watching her." The other man told him as he had watched all the wrecks that took place on the road.

> ❧ Inside Ny's House

Ny comes walking inside, and her parents, Joe and Gail Baker, and her two little brothers, Billy and Gary, are waiting at the dinner table. Mr. Baker is a little upset at Ny.

"Where have you been? You're almost a half hour late for dinner." Mr. Blake asked her, looking at his watch.

"I stopped to talk to a friend, and he held me up, then I saw a car crash into the back of another one. It may not have happened if one of the drivers wasn't been looking at me.

Didn't I tell you that your clothes are too tight, and one of these days, some guy is going to mistake you for a grown woman," Mr. Baker said. He wasn't happy to hear all this.

"You are going to get yourself and whatever man you're within a whole lot of trouble. And the reason I say that is because you have too many boys calling the house, and that is getting ready to stop! Do you understand me, young lady?" He continued, trying to explain to her, hoping that she would at least listen to him this time.

"Yes, sir! But I will be 16 next week," Ny replied. The feeling that every boy craves her beauty satisfies her like anything.

"Now, what is that supposed to mean? Do you think you're all grown up now? Because if so, I'm going to start letting you pay the rent and the bills." Mr. Baker replied, giving her a stern look.

"No daddy! I don't mean that at all. You said, "that you would buy me a car for my 16 birthday." Ny replied. She would never pay the bills and rent for sure.

"I know what I said, but now I see that you are so boy crazy. What I look like is buying you a car, so you can go give your little pussy away. Then come back with a baby that you can't take care of.

"Your father is right! You have just too many boys calling the house, and I'm not going to be taking care of my babies and yours too." Mrs. Blake said.

"I would not do anything like that. I have my whole life to look forward too." Ny said.

"Every time I heard a girl say that! A year later, she had a baby." Mrs. Baker replied.

"Come on, mama, I promise," Ny promised her mother.

"Well, show your dad that you can stop having all of these boys calling the house; we just might get you a car and me." Mrs. Baker said.

"Thanks, mom and dad. You will not be disappointed." Ny said excitedly and jumped off the sofa to hug her.

As Ny hugs her mother, right then the phone rings, Mr. Baker answers it.

"Hello!" Mr. Baker said as soon as she answered the phone.

"Hello! May I speak to Ni?" The other side on the other side said.

"Who in the hell is this?" Mr. Baker said in a higher tone. She lost her temper to hear a boy's voice on the other side.

"Are you her man?" The voice on the other side said. The call was from Lorenzo.

"Hell no! I am not her man! I am her father, and who are you?" Mr. Baker yelled. He couldn't bare random men calling at his home willing to talk to his daughter.

"My name is Lorenzo. I am the guy she met about an hour ago." Lorenzo told Mr. Baker.

"Well, she is busy now, and she will talk to you later." Mr. Baker replied aggressively and slammed down the phone.

He then turned to Ny and sternly said, "This is the very thing I am talking about, having these different guys calling the house. And who is this, Lorenzo?"

"He's…. a friend," Ny replied in a lower tone.

"A friend! A friend!" Mr. Baker yelled. "How in the hell could he be a friend when he said he just met you less than an hour ago? Now I understand why you were late. And lately, you have been starting to lie, and that is something that I will not put up with because if you lie, you will steal, and if you steal, then you will set somebody up to get killed." He continued. Mr. Baker was really mad at Ny this time. He tried his best to explain to Ny about the world full of men, but she just wouldn't understand.

"That's right! Your father and I work too hard to try and give you and your brothers a good life, believe it or not. But, you could tell a lie to the wrong person and could lose everything you got, including your life. So if you want us to buy you a car? Stop having so many boys calling our house, and for your sake. Stop lying! Please!" Mrs. Baker pleaded.

"Okay," Ny said with a lowered head.

II

❧ A Week Later – Ny's Birthday

$\mathcal{N}$y wakes up in the morning and looks out the window. To her surprise, she sees a 76 Camaro outside, with a ribbon wrapped around it. Ny immediately jumps out of her bed and runs out of her bedroom as fast as she can. In her excitement, she forgot that she still had on her PJs; she ran out of the house and jumped in behind the wheel of the car. Her mother and father came out behind her.

"Thanks, mom and dad! I really love both of you!" Ny exclaimed. She couldn't control her excitement.

"Thank your mother because if it were up to me, you would not have this car, but your mother talked me into it. I just hope you meant what you said last week." Mr. Baker replied with a smile on his face.

"Oh! I do!" Ny said.

About a week later, Ny got her driving license and decided to ride down the street. Having a movie plan with Lorenzo, she pulls her car into a movie theater.

After reaching there, she gets out of the car and walks in. Ni's face lights up as she sees Lorenzo waiting for her. He walks up to her, hugs and kisses Ny passionately.

"So, what do you want to see?" Lorenzo asked Ni.

"I don't want to see anything but you back in bed again like we were last night," Ny replied in a lower and more romantic voice.

"Hmm That sounds real fun to me." He replied and winked at Ni.

"I am going to ride with you because I told my parents that I was coming here, and they think I am a big liar, and I would not put it pass them riding by just to see if my car was parked here," Ny said.

"Well, you are lying," Lorenzo said, lifting up one of his eyebrows. A smirk covered his face as he kept looking at Ni.

"Well, what would you want me to tell them? That I am going over to Lorenzo's house to give him some pussy just like I did last night." Ny giggled and said.

"Alright! Let's go." Lorenzo said, holding her hand and kissing it gently. Inside Lorenzo's Parent's House Downstairs in the basement, where Lorenzo's bedroom is, they just finished making love and are getting dressed. Lorenzo goes into the bathroom while Ny is in her underwear, walking around his room, being nosey, and looking in his closet. She opens his drawers and starts moving things around on his dresser, finding his wallet.

She opens it up and sees his driver's license. When she looks at the date of birth, it says 1955. Ny is left shocked.

"How come you lied to me about how old you were?" Ny said, holding his license.

"If I would have told you the truth. You might have told me that I was too old for you, and you are so fine; I just could not take that chance." Lorenzo said, taking the license from her hand.

"Well, what's done is done, and by the way, my father wants to meet you. He told me to bring you by after we come from the show." Ny shrugged her shoulders and said.

"I can't meet your father. He might have me thrown in jail once he finds out how old I am." Lorenzo said. He was certain that Ni's father would know about his real age and might throw him behind bars.

"Well, he thinks you are 17, and that is what you told me, so that is what I told him. I promised my parents that I would not have a lot of boys calling the house, and I would just talk to one if they bought me a car, and they did. So now I have to hold up my end, and you are the one I choose to be with. But if you don't meet my father, you can say goodbye to me forever." Ny replied in a convincing tone.

As they were having a conversation, Lorenzo couldn't take his eyes off Ni.

She stood there in a sexy black bra and underwear. Ny smiles and turns her back towards Lorenzo, and bends over slowly to pick up her pants. As she bents down,

Lorenzo got excited. Ny starts wearing her pants, but she acts like she is having trouble getting them on.

"Could you please help me get these jeans on? I have trouble sometimes getting them over this big fat round ass." Ny said, pretending she was having trouble wearing her pants.

Lorenzo, who was waiting for a call, ran over to Ni. Without wasting a single minute, he starts kissing her neck and squeezing her big chest. Instead of helping Ny with her pants up, he pulled them down and put her back in the bed, and started making love to her.

"You better hurry up because if I'm not home at a certain time, my father is going to get angry, and by the way. Ny said, moaning. "You have not been wearing any condoms. What's gonna happened if I get pregnant?" Ny asked Lorenzo. She was quite concerned about it.

"Don't worry about babes! I got it under control." He said and continued making love.

❧ Inside The Baker's House:

Ny enters her home along with Lorenzo. Mr. Baker wanted to meet him.

"Hi, mom and dad." Ny greeted her parents as she entered with Lorenzo. "This is Lorenzo." She continues, introducing Lorenzo to her parents.

"How are you?" Her parents asked Lorenzo.

"I am fine, and it is really nice to meet both of you," Lorenzo replied. He was quite nervous.

"Well, Lorenzo, Ny tells me you are the captain of your football team. What high school do you attend? I would like to come to watch you play because I'm a big football fan." Mr. Baker asks Lorenzo.

Lorenzo is caught off guard with a dumb look on his face.

"I was the captain, but I got hurt and had to quit playing football." He replied.

"That's too bad. Sorry to hear that. But I do get tickets to the Giants games. Maybe one day you would like to go with me?" Mr. Baker said. He was quite sorry to hear that.

"That sounds good. Looking forward to it." Lorenzo smiled and replied.

"What is your last name?" Mrs. Baker asked him.

"Dellwood. But I have to go now. I promised my mother I would help her do something, and it was nice meeting you all. Goodbye!" Lorenzo said.

"Goodbye, and drive safe." Mr. and Mrs. Blake said.

Ny walks Lorenzo to his car. Lorenzo is mad and upset.

"Why in the hell did you tell your father that I was the captain of the football team? Hell, I don't even like football. I don't watch it, and I for damn sure don't know how to play it. Your father wants me to go to a game with him, hell I don't even know the rules, and the only teams I know are the ones in New York; what are the names of some of the other teams? St. Louis Seahawks, Tampa Bay Bulls?" Lorenzo said. He was quite pissed off about why Ny said this.

"The Bulls are basketball. Your right! You don't know shit. The first guy I ever met and didn't know anything about sports." Ny said she, too, was surprised that he doesn't know anything about football.

"Next time! Please check with me before you lie to me." Lorenzo said as he moved toward his car.

"Okay, baby!" Ny replied with a cute smile.

Ny gives Lorenzo a kiss to calm him down. Lorenzo gets in his car and drives off.

III

❧ Two Months Later-Inside The Baker's House

There are allot of men watching the football game. There is a knock on the door, and Mr. Baker opens the door, and it is Lorenzo.

"How are you doing, Lorenzo? Ny went with her mother. They should be back in 30 minutes, come on in and meet some of her cousins and uncles." Mr. Baker said, letting Lorenzo into the house.

Mr. Baker walks Lorenzo back to where they are looking at the football game.

"Hey everybody! This is Ni's boyfriend, and he used to be captain of his football team before he got hurt and had to quit." Mr. Blake said as he introduced Lorenzo to the guests.

"What happened?" An uncle said, looking at Lorenzo.

"Um Nothing. I just had knee surgery." Lorenzo replied. He made up this story as he couldn't come up with some other story.

"What position did you play?" The other uncle asked him, taking an interest in how Lorenzo played football, which he actually never did!

"I played all of them," Lorenzo said as he was quite confused about what to say.

Everybody became real quiet and looked at each other. Then look at Lorenzo.

Lorenzo was getting really nervous, then they all started laughing.

"Can you believe this guy? He plays all of them. Well, when your knee gets well, maybe you can help out the Giants because these Rams are just kicking their asses all over the place. HA! HA! Oh, by the way, do you have a job?" Uncle asked Lorenzo, showing interest in him.

"Yes, I work at the gas station two blocks down the street on Pine and Grand," Lorenzo replied.

"Well, why don't you quit and go join the Giants because even with your bad knee, you could play better than what they have out there right now. HA! HA!" The first uncle said sarcastically.

Lorenzo kind of bonded with the first uncle, but what he didn't know was that Uncle 1 was a Rams fan. The Rams scored a touchdown, and uncle 1 jumped up, cheering, and so did Lorenzo. Lorenzo noticed that no one else was happy but himself and uncle 1. When Lorenzo looked around wasn't anybody smiling, and Mr. Baker gave him a look that would kill him.

"Where in the hell are you from cheering for them damn Rams? Hey Joe? I thought you said he was the captain of his football team. What kind of captain is he if he is going against the home team? Acting like that. It would not surprise me if it was his own teammate that messed up his knee. I don't even want to be around this dude anymore." One of Ni's cousins said.

Right then, the front door opened, and it was Ny and her mother. Lorenzo felt relieved because he had an excuse to get away.

"It was nice meeting everybody, and I hope to see you all again." Lorenzo sighed in relief and said. They all looked at him with disgust, and nobody said anything except for uncle 1.

"Hey there, young brother, don't pay them no mind. You were cheering for the right team HA! HA!" Uncle 1 said he couldn't control his laughter.

"That's right, take your soft ass back in there with the rest of the women." Ni's cousin said, joining the conversation.

Lorenzo ran quickly over to Ni.

"Hey, I got to go. Your family is rubbing me the wrong way." Lorenzo said.

He couldn't stay there anymore.

"What happened?" Ny asked. She couldn't understand why he wanted to leave.

"I cheered for the wrong team," Lorenzo replied, closing his eyes tight out of embarrassment.

Ny looked at him for a while and then burst out into laughter. "That will do it. Okay baby, I will be over later."

Lorenzo leaves, and Ny walks into the bathroom. Ny pulls out a pregnancy kit, and after a few minutes, it shows that she is pregnant. Ny became really nervous and started crying. Not thinking, she flushed the strip down the toilet and threw the box away in the bathroom trash can.

Later that evening, Mrs. Baker went to clean the bathroom. She empties the trash by pulling out the clear plastic bag. At first, she didn't notice the pregnancy box. It wasn't until she took the bag outside that it caught her attention. She dropped the trash. Reached inside the bag and pulled out the pregnancy box, and ran back into the house, yelling and screaming for Ni.

"Ny! Ny! Ny! Where in the hell are you, Ny?" Mrs. Baker screamed her lungs out. She was furious to see the kit, and several questions lined up in her mind.

Ny was in her room, sleeping soundly. Mrs. Baker entered her room in a rush and woke her up.

"What in the hell is this? Please tell me you are not pregnant?" Mrs. Baker asked furiously. She was concerned and mad at the same time.

Hearing this and seeing her mother's outrageous eyes, Ny started crying and said after a while, "I went to the free clinic, and they told me I was. I didn't believe them, so I bought the pregnancy test box, and it said the same thing."

"Is it Lorenzo's?" Mrs. Bakers asked her.

"Yes," Ny said softly.

"Get your ass up. We are going over to his house right now!" Mrs. Baker said.

She needed to get things cleared up with him before it was way too late.

ꙮ Outside Of Lorenzo's House

Mrs. Baker and Ny are at the front door. Mrs. Dellwood Lorenzo's mother opens the door.

Lorenzo's mother, Mrs. Dellwood, opened the door and politely said, "Hello! May I help you?"

"You damn right you can help me! Your son Lorenzo has gotten my daughter pregnant, and I want to know what you all want to do about it?" Mrs. Baker said furiously. She couldn't calm herself down as her 16-year-old's life was at risk.

"Wait a minute. You're trying to tell me that my son has gotten this little girl pregnant. She can't be any more than 16 years old." Mrs. Dellwood asked. She was shocked to hear what Mrs. Baker was saying.

"That is exactly what I am telling you. Hell! Don't you know what's going on in your house with your child?" Ny's mother said out of frustration.

"Child! Lorenzo is a 25-year-old grown man. He lives downstairs, and I live upstairs, and what he does is his own business." Mrs. Dellwood said, revealing her real age of Lorenzo.

When Mrs. Baker heard that, she almost fainted, then she looked really hard at Ny.

"Ny! Did you know how old Lorenzo was?" Mrs. Baker asked Ny sternly. Her blood was boiling, and there was no way she would let Lorenzo get away with this.

"At first, I didn't. He told me he was 17, but I saw his driver's license one day and found out the truth; by then, we had already started having sex with each other, so I felt like it didn't matter." Ny replied softly.

"Now that you are pregnant! Do you still think it doesn't matter?" Mrs. Baker said.

"You mean to tell me that my son outright lie to you about his age." Mrs. Dellwood said. She was shocked to hear that her son actually lied about his age.

"Yes, he did," Ny replied. She kept her head lower and kept looking at the ground.

"Please come on in and have a seat. I'm going to go get Lorenzo." Mrs. Dellwood said politely, letting them both in the house.

After a while, Lorenzo enters the front room and is shocked to see Ny and Mrs. Baker. Before he could say anything, Mrs. Dellwood began the conversation.

"Did you lie to this little girl about your age?" Mrs. Dellwood asked Lorenzo.

She was quite disappointed about what he did. Lorenzo held his head down and didn't say anything.

"You hear me talking to you, boy! Did you lie to this little girl about your age?" Mrs. Dellwood yelled. She was furious about all he did.

"Yes, I did," Lorenzo answered.

"You are one dumb ass man. Don't you know you could go to jail for something like this? Is a little piece of pussy worth it?" Mrs. Dellwood replied.

"Well, he is getting ready to find out, but first, I'm going to go back home and talk to my husband and see if he wants to press charges. But one thing I want to say to you, Lorenzo, is that you are one sorry excuse for a man. We welcomed you into our home and let you date our daughter, and in return, you lie to us and maybe mess up my daughter's future just so you can get your rocks off. You are a lousy son of a bitch, and I hope you burn in hell, you punk ass mother fucker! Come on, Ny, let's go!" Mrs. Baker said angrily.

"I am sorry and ashamed." Mrs. Dellwood replied. She was embarrassed at what her son had done. Mrs. Baker didn't say, just started crying as she was leaving.

❧ Inside The Baker's House

Ny and Mrs. Baker are sitting in the kitchen, and Mr. Baker comes walking in. He's in a good mood until he sees the look on their faces.

"What in hell is wrong with you two?" Mr. Baker asked as he saw their gloomy faces.

"Ny is pregnant by Lorenzo." Mrs. Baker said in a heavy tone.

"What! I told you this was going to happen. We never should have bought that car. Well, that is what kids do." Mr. Baker angrily said.

"Lorenzo is not a kid." Mrs. Baker said. She had too much information about Lorenzo. All that was still unknown to Mr. Baker.

"What do you mean he is not a kid?" Mr. Baker asked. He was confused about what his wife was saying.

"Lorenzo is a 25-year-old grown man." Mrs. Baker continued. She was going red out of anger.

When Mr. Baker heard that, he hit the roof. Jumping up and down, yelling and screaming. Ny was terrified because she had never seen her father act like this before.

"I am going to kill that mother fucker! He came into my house and lied to me, ate my food, and took advantage of my daughter. I am going to kill that mother fucker!" Mr. Baker yelled at the top of his lungs. Furious with what he had just heard, Mr. Baker went into his bedroom. He returned in a few minutes with a gun in his hand. Mrs. Baker sees this and stops him from going out of the house. She makes him sit down because he is really upset.

"Don't go out there and do anything that is stupid that will get your ass thrown in jail." Mrs. Baker warned him.

"Your right! I got to plan this." Mr. Baker said.

"That's not what I am talking about. We are going to let the police handle this." Ny's mother said. She didn't want her husband to get into any kind of trouble.

"Fuck the police! I am going to handle this my way, and I mean, don't call them! Understood!" Mr. Baker said there was no way he would sit back and have dinner with ease. He had to do something about what Lorenzo had done to his daughter.

"Joe! You promised me long ago, before Ny was born that you would leave that gangster shit alone if I married you." Mrs. Baker said. She tried her best to stop her husband from doing any hideous crime.

"And I have, Gail." Mr. Baker turned to his wife and said.

"So what are you going to do now? Get on the phone and call your two gangster brothers, Big Al, and Billy, because you know they still live that life, and I'm surprised that they are still walking around." Mrs. Baker said.

"I am a man. That is my little girl. This is a total shock; just let me have a couple of days to think about it." Mr. Baker replied. His eyes were red out of rage.

"Okay! I will go along with that, but please don't do anything stupid because two wrongs don't make a right." Said Mrs. Baker. She didn't want her husband to get into any kind of trouble.

Mr. Baker got up from his seat and handed the gun to his wife, then went downstairs into his office and got on the phone.

"What's up, Big Al? This is your brother Joe." Mr. Baker said as Big Al picked up the call.

"What can I do for you, big brother? You sound like something is on your mind. I almost didn't catch your voice." Big Al said.

"Do you have any throw always?" Mr. Baker asked.

"Yea! You know I keep them. What do you need it for?" Big Al asked. He was quite clueless about why Mr. Baker was asking him about all this all of a sudden.

"Ny is pregnant, and I am going to take out her boyfriend." Mr. Baker replied.

He was quite frustrated at that time.

"Come on now, Joe! Kids are going to be kids." Big Al said, unknown about the age of Lorenzo.

"Lorenzo is not a kid, but a 25-year-old man who came into my house and lied to me and my wife and took full advantage of my daughter." Mr. Baker replied with anger.

"Oh! In that case, he got to go. So when do you want to do this?" Big Al said.

Now he was quite aware of why Mr. Baker was so pissed off.

"Tonight. He gets off at 10:00 pm. Call Billy and tell him to bring his van and meet us at Daves at 9:30, and don't be late." Mr. Blake explained to Big Al what to do next and how to get prepared for tonight.

Mr. Baker hung up the phone and then called one of his friends, Brad Jones, who has a farm outside of New York City.

"Hello! Brad, this is Joe Baker, and I am calling to take you up on that favor." Mr. Baker said to Brad.

"What can I do for you?" Brad asked him.

"I need to use your grinder around 12 midnight." Mr. Baker asked Brad.

However, he did not reveal why he needed that.

"Anytime, because if wasn't for you. I would have been dead and gone a long time ago. See you when you get here." Brad answered. He did not ask the reason why he wanted that grinder.

"Thanks." Mr. Baker said.

IV

9:00 pm: Mr. Baker is leaving out the door, and his wife stops him.

"Where are you going?" Mrs. Baker asked.

"Going up to Dave's and meeting some the guys from work to have a drink and relax and get some of this shit off of my mind." Mr. Baker replied. He was all set and prepared with his plan to get down on Lorenzo at 10 pm.

"Well, be careful, and remember what I said." Mrs. Baker said, reminding him that he has to keep himself away from the call of crime. Mr. Baker didn't say anything, just looked at his wife real hard, then walked out the door.

Outside Of Dave's Bar Joe's brothers Billy and Big Al pull up in the van. Joe hops in, and they pull off.

"Hey, Joe! Big Al was telling me that Ni's boyfriend is 25 years old." Billy said.

"That's right, and that is why I'm going to kill his ass. Pull up over here, and we are going to wait for him to come out. It's almost ten, and he should be coming out any minute. Speak of the devil; here he comes. Wait until he gets into his car and pulls off, and we will catch him at the next block." Mr. Baker replied.

Lorenzo gets into his car and pulls off. Billy catches up to him at the next block. Joe is sitting in the passenger seat. Joe rolls down the window and flags over Lorenzo. Lorenzo looks nervous but pulls over.

"How are you doing, Lorenzo? I want to talk to you man-to-man about Ny's pregnancy. Leave your car parked here and hop in the back of the van and we are going to go have a drink at Dave's; after all, you are old enough to drink, right!" Mr. Baker said, trying to control his anger. Lorenzo gets out of his car and walks into the van. Then Billy pulls off.

"Mr. Baker, I am truly sorry for what I have done," Lorenzo said. He was quite ashamed of what had happened and what he did with Ny.

"Not as sorry as you are going to be." Mr. Baker said angrily. Mr. Baker gets out of the passenger seat and walks to the back of the van, and punches Lorenzo.

Then Big Al punches Lorenzo. Then the both of the start beating the hell out of Lorenzo. He is crying and begging them to stop.

"You made a fool out of me by lying to me and my family and took full advantage of my daughter, and I am going to make sure that never happens again."

Mr. Baker said he was angry and frustrated with what Lorenzo had done.

They beat Lorenzo until he was unconscious. When he came to, they were pulling up on Brad's farm. Billy parks the van, and Mr. Baker and Big Al drag Lorenzo out of the van. Lorenzo is really scared now.

"Please! Please don't hurt me anymore!" Lorenzo begged for forgiveness. He was quite scared of what was happening to him.

"You might as well pray because you're leaving here today. Give it to me, Big Al." Mr. Baker said. He was burning to avenge Lorenzo as he had played with his little girl, lying about his age and taking full advantage of Ni.

Big Al hands Joe the gun, and Joe points the gun at Lorenzo and fires four shots into his head, killing Lorenzo. Brad hears the shots and comes running out of the house.

"Hello there, old friend. I didn't know you were out here until I heard the shots." Brad said. Everybody shakes hands.

"Do you think anybody else heard these shots?" Billy asked Brad. They didn't want any police thing around the scene.

"No. Don't worry! My neighbors are miles away. But what we need to do now strip him of his clothes so I can burn them and then send him thru the grinder. I will mix up his remains with concrete and pour it into a hole I dug and cover it up with grass sod, and this is one body they will never find. They all started laughing and shaking their heads.

"I pray that there never comes a day that I piss you off," Billy said.

"I don't know you, but I have heard my brother speak about you sometimes.

What is going through my mind is what made you put yourself out like this? I'm going to be honest; everybody will not do what you are doing now! Please tell me?" Big Al asked Brad.

Brad turned to Joe (Mr. Baker) to ask, "Is it okay to tell him?"

Joe nods his head, saying yes.

"20 Years ago, your brother walked in on a drug deal that went bad. There were two guys that were getting ready to kill me; before they could do it, Joe pulled out his gun and shot and killed both of them. I told him I would always be in his debt because if it were not for him, I would be a dead man right now." Brad told Billy.

"I feel you on that one." Big Al joined the conversation.

"Shiddddd!!! So do I. HA! HA!" Billy said and laughed, thinking of what Brad was telling Billy.

"Come on, brothers; I want to get back home before Gail starts getting suspicious." Mr. Baker said he was in a hurry to finish the work and go home. He didn't want his wife to suspect him.

"Hey, Joe! Do you think you will feel bad about this later on in life?" Billy said.

"Hell no!" Mr. Baker answered without wasting a single moment.

"Why not?" Billy asked. He wanted to know what made him this mad to commit this action.

"He was a Rams fan, and fuck anybody who ain't for the home team." Mr. Baker replied.

They all started laughing. Billy and Big Al get back into the van. Brad and Mr. Baker say their goodbyes. Mr. Baker gets into the van, and they pull off.

❧ Inside The Bakers House – 2 weeks later.

Mrs. Baker is reading the newspaper, and she sees an article where Lorenzo Dellwood has been missing. She gets suspicious and shows the paper to Mr. Baker.

"Have you seen this?" Mrs. Baker asked her husband. She wanted to make sure that he wasn't behind the boy being missing.

"No! But I would bet anything he is not missing, but on the run, because is ass was on his way to jail." Mr. Baker replied. He ensured to keep himself calm and let Mrs. Baker doubt him at any cost. "It says here that they found his car a block from where he works." Mrs. Baker said. She was still convinced of what her husband was saying. Mrs. Baker looks at Mr. Baker with a disgusting look on her face.

"Please tell me that you didn't do anything to that man." Mrs. Baker continued as she saw her husband wasn't replying.

"I told you the same thing I told the police when they came by last week." Mr. Baker replied.

"How come you didn't tell me that the police came by?" Mrs. Baker said. She seemed excited now. All she was curious about was knowing that her husband had nothing to do with the boy's sudden disappearance.

"It was the same day you went with Ny to get her abortion, and I didn't want to upset you with that."

"What did they say?" She asked.

"Well, they were making their rounds to all of his known associates. Lorenzo's mother told them about the pregnancy, and I could be a suspect if foul play was involved. I told the police that we were going to let the law handle it, and you told Lorenzo to his face that he was going to jail. So when he heard that, I guess he made a run for it. The police seemed to be satisfied with my answer, and one of them said to me." If some 25-year-old man had gotten my 16-year-old daughter pregnant, I would want to kill him myself" Then they left. Do me a favor and call Ny in here for me." Mr. Baker answered.

"Ni! Come in here. Your father wants you." Mrs. Baker calls out on her daughter.

"Yes daddy," Ny said as she came out of her bedroom.

"Have you seen or heard from Lorenzo? Because the police came by here asking questions." Mr. Baker asked Ni.

"No, I have not," Ny replied. She wasn't sure why her father asked this question out of the blue.

"You see what I mean. He knocked you up, and now you can't find him. It ain't no telling how many girls he has done this to. You can't keep on getting abortions, so tomorrow your mother is going to take you to the doctor so you can get some birth control pills, and you better take them because the next time your ass comes up pregnant, get ready to pack your bags because we are going to drop you off at the Salvation Army. Understood?" Mr. Baker said. He tried his best to wipe off his name from her daughter's mind forever.

"Yes sir," Ny replied.

"Come on, Gail I'm ready to eat, and by the way, Ni, I heard that the sleeping arrangements and food are not all that good at the Salvation Army." Mr. Baker told his daughter.

Ny has a real sad look on her face as she walks into the kitchen to eat. She has no idea her father has killed Lorenzo, making him pay for what he did to her. Ni's parents tried their best to help her mend her ways, but it was Ny, and she never listened to any of her parents.

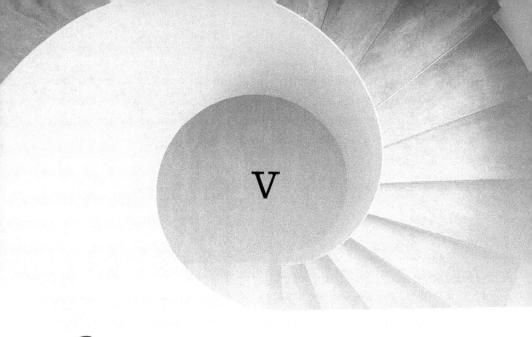

V

*Y*ears passed by, and Ny was still in her games to dating different men in her life. Staying with a single man and living peacefully was not her piece of cake. Mr. and Mrs. Baker tried their best to help their daughter get straight on the path, but this was something she wasn't interested in doing.

❧ 8 Years Later: Inside Ni's Apartment –

Eight years have passed, and Ny has changed a lot in the past eight years. She was now a grown woman, engaged to a man named Jay, who loved her deeply. Jay was a successful man who took care of Ny and gave her everything she could ever want. But despite all of that, Ny was secretly cheating on him. She is living with him in the house.

Ny cleaning and dusting. In walks her fiancé Jay. He has an angry look on his face.

"I have been calling you? Why haven't you answered the phone? I hope you are not messing around with me again, are you?" Jay said angrily.

"No, I am not! I told you that was a one-time thing, and it will never happen again." Ny replied. She was scared as Jay had some serious anger issues.

"Okay then, tell me, who is that dude?" Jay said. Besides having anger issues, he would always suspect Ni.

"What, dude?" Ny asked. She wasn't aware of what he was talking about.

"The one that comes here on the motorcycle when I'm at work." He replied in a fit of rage.

"Oh! That ain't nobody but my cousin Jeff." Ny replied when she figured out who Jay was talking about.

"Jeff! Who in the hell is Jeff? I never heard you speak about no cousin named Jeff." Jay replied, filled with rage. He couldn't stand Ny talking to any other man.

Ny had always been a flirtatious girl, and as she got older, her flirtatiousness turned into something more dangerous. She couldn't resist the attention of other men, even though she loved Jay with all her heart. She knew that what she was doing was wrong, but she couldn't help herself.

Ny had always been a flirtatious girl, and as she got older, her flirtatiousness turned into something more dangerous. She couldn't resist the attention of other men, even though she loved Jay with all her heart. She knew that what she was doing was wrong, but she couldn't help herself.

"Jeff's my 2nd cousin from Atlanta on my mother's side. His job just transferred him to New York a week ago, and he looked me up.

"I hope you're not lying to me because I'm trying my best to make this work.

You are out of a job, Ny, and I'm taking care of all of these bills myself. I love you so much, and I would do anything for you. I just hope you're not making a fool out of me." Jay said, calming himself down. He loved Ny and couldn't afford to lose her at any cost.

"I made one mistake; I'm not going to make another." Ny stepped forward and held Jay's hand.

They gave each other a kiss and went into the bedroom. The next morning, Jay leaves for work, and 10 minutes after he is gone, there is a knock on the door, and it is Jeff. Ny lets him in, and they go into the guest bedroom. At 12 noon, her phone rings. It was Jay. Ny picks up the phone.

"Hey baby! What are you doing?" Jay said.

Ny is making love to Jeff. She puts her finger over her mouth for Jeff to shut up.

"Oh, nothing, just cooking and watching T.V.," Ny lies to Jay.

"What are you cooking?" Jay asks, believing what she said. He was unaware of the fact that she was cheating on her.

"Oh, it is a surprise?" Ny said.

"Alright! I'll see you when I get home. Goodbye!" Jay said and disconnected the call.

Ny hangs up the phone and continues to make love to Jeff. It's 5:30 pm, and Jay comes walking in.

"Hey baby! I am really hungry. What is the surprise?" Jay called out to Ni. He was quite hungry, excited to see what Ny had cooked for him.

"I'm sorry, baby. I fell asleep and burned up the pot roast. Can we go out to eat?" Ny said. She again wasn't being honest with him.

"Where is the pot roast you burnt?" Jay asked; he wanted to see what the surprise was.

But Ny was quite smart to handle it all, and she said, "I wrapped it up in a bag and dropped it into the dumpster before it smelled the place up.

"Okay! That was smart. So now, where do you want to go eat?" Jay asked Ni, wrapping his arms around her.

It's 7:45, and Jay and Ny are walking back into the apartment, coming from eating out.

"Thanks, baby, that was too good," Ny said.

"I will do anything I can for my woman. And one thing I'm going to do is take out the trash like a good man should because today is Tuesday, and the trash men come every Wednesday early in the morning." Jay said. He wanted to give all the happiness and smiles to Ni. But little did he know that Ny was cheating on him with Jeff.

Jay takes the trash to the dumpster and opens it up, and it is empty. This catches Jay's attention. Then he remembers the letter in the mail from the trash company saying that the trash day is going to be switched from early Wednesday to early Tuesday. Jay sees that the only trash in the dumpster is what he threw in there.

Jay starts thinking about where is the burnt-up pot roast.

Jay walks back into the apartment and hears the shower running. He cracks the bathroom door and sees Ny getting into the shower. Jay goes into the living room and picks up the phone, and calls his job, letting them know he will not be at work tomorrow. Jay leaves at his regular time as if he is going to work. Jay parks his car in the mall garage and catches a taxi back to the coffee house down the street from his house. Jay sat by the window and watched to see who would come over.

Jay ordered a cup of coffee and a donut, and 5 minutes later, Jeff pulled up on his motorcycle, knocked on the door, and Ny let him in. Jay waits about 10 minutes, then walks up to his front door and puts his ear to it. He doesn't hear anything, so he slowly opens the door. He doesn't see anybody in the front room; now, he is tiptoeing back toward the bedroom. The closer he gets he can hear moaning and other sounds of passion coming from the guest bedroom. Jay opens up the door and sees Ny and Jeff making love. They are going at it so hard that they don't know that Jay is in the room. Jay gets mad out of anger. He's really mad.

"You fucking bitch! I ought to kill your ass! So this is supposed to be your cousin Jeff. Look more like kissing cousins. No! Let me take that back. More like fucking cousins." Jay yelled in a fit of rage.

Ny pulls the covers over her head, and Jeff jumps up.

"Look, man! She told me she lived with her brother. There is no way in hell I would come over to another man's house and have sex with his woman." Jeff told Jay what Ny had told him when they met. He, too, was quite shocked at what had suddenly happened.

"Ni! Is this true?" Jay turned to Ny and asked her if it was true. He was quite startled to know what Ny had told Jeff about their relationship. Ny didn't say anything. Jay pulled the covers off of her. Then reaches over and slaps her.

"Is this true? Answer me bitch!" Jay asks her again, expecting an answer this time. Ny still didn't say anything; they just started crying. Jay then turns toward Jeff.

"Hey, man! I can't be mad at you. It's not your fault she is a lying ass bitch, and one day she is going to get somebody killed. I tell you what? If you want her?

You can have her. I'm not going to have anything else to do with this slut. This is the 2nd time she cheated on me, and I'll be damn if it's going to be a 3rd." Jay said in a quite annoyed tone. He has had enough of Ny and her addiction to get laid before every other man.

Jay walks into their bedroom and throws all of Ni's belonging into a suitcase he had in a closet. Walked to the front door, opened it, and threw Ni's belonging out on the streets. Jay walked back into his bedroom, pulled out a gun, and pointed it at Ni. When Jeff saw that, he ran out of the apartment.

"You have 1 minute to get your slut, bitch, and hoe ass out of here, or I am going to pull the trigger," Jay said, pointing a gun toward her.

Ny jumped up, put on her jogging pants, housecoat, and shoes, and ran out of the apartment. Jay slams the door behind her. Ny picks up the suitcase and starts walking down the street, and Jeff is nowhere to be found. Ny turns the corner, and there is Jeff sitting on his motorcycle.

"Well, I guess you're going to have to come with me?" Jeff asked her, seeing her carry all her stuff.

"I'll guess so," Ny replies, shrugging her shoulders. She wasn't sure where to go.

Ny hops on the back of Jeff's motorcycle with the suitcase in her hand. They pull up in front of Jeff's place. He doesn't live in the best neighborhood in the world, but it is not the worst either. Ny walks in and realizes that this is not all of the comforts of home, but it's better than being homeless.

"So where do I put my suitcase?" Ny asked Jeff.

"In the bedroom straight ahead," Jeff replies.

"Where are the bus stops? I am going to get up in the morning and go find a job." Ny said she was now worried about making a living. Back there with Jay, all she had to do was stay at home.

"There is one at the end of the block," Jeff told her.

The next day Ny is standing at the bus stop. A car rides by and then backs up.

The man rolls his window down and starts talking to Ny.

"Hello! How are you doing? My name is Don Greybrook, and yours." The man in the car asks Ny.

"My name is Nigeria, but everyone calls me Ny," Ny replies with a smile.

"I normally don't stop to talk to strangers at the bus stop, but you have to be the finest woman I have ever seen. Please tell me that you are not married." Don said in a flirtiest manner.

"No, I'm not. I do have a friend, but it's nothing serious." Ny replies. She tells him about her being single.

"Just what I wanted to hear. Would you like a ride to where ever you're going?" Don said, offering Ny a ride in his luxurious car.

Ny is tempted to take the ride because the man is well-dressed and driving a nice expensive car. Her heart races as she thinks about the man's offer. All she could think of at that time was getting a well-paid job. Ny was aware that looking back at Jay would never be any more.

"I would love too, but I am job hunting, and I really don't have the time," Ny tells him, making a gloomy face.

"Well, young lady, today maybe your lucky day. I'm the Asst. Manager at Leu Motor Company. Here is my I.D. How would you like to start off with 15 dollars an hour plus benefits." Don offered her a job in his company.

Ny couldn't believe what she was hearing. A real big smile came on her face.

Then a sad look came across her face, and Don was wondering what was wrong.

"Leu Motors is on the other side of town. I don't have a car, and it would take me too long to get there. Thanks but no thanks." Ny told Don.

"Don't worry about that. I own some apartments two miles away from the plant. You can catch the bus and be there in 10 minutes. I will let you have the first month's rent free, and then it would be $400.00 a month, and depending on how we get along, it may not cost you anything. You know what I mean." Don said, highlighting all the perks Ny would get if she got along well with him.

"I know what you mean. I am a big girl, and I know how the game is played.

But we will take it one day at a time just to see how things go." Ny replies.

"Agreed! Well, hop in, and let's go get you your job." Don excitedly said and gave her a lift to the office.

Ny is pleased to get a job without wasting any time. She hops in the car, and they pull off.

❧ Inside Leu Motors

Ny is sitting in an office. Don comes walking toward her with some papers in his hand. He hands them to Ny, Don points to the door, and they walk out together.

"I cut through all the red tape, and you will show up for orientation next Monday at 9:00 am. The apartment will be ready this Friday, and here is my car phone number. If you need me to come pick you up? Call me." Don said, expecting to take their relationship to a suitable advantage.

"I will get one of my cousins to drop me off," Ny said.

"Okay! I will show you the apartment you will be staying in, and I will meet you there at Noon Friday." Don replies, agreeing with Ni's decision.

Ny has Don drop her off back at the bus stop. Ny gives Don a hug and a kiss.

Then they looked each other in the eye, then Ny gave Don a real passionate kiss. Ny thanks Don, then she gets out of the car. Don just can't take his eyes off Ny walking down the street. The only thing that made him move was the other cars blowing at him, and some of them were blowing at Ny.

꙳   Inside Jeff's House:

Ny and Jeff are eating dinner.

"I found a job today." Ny gives the good news to Jeff.

"Oh yea! Where at?" Jeff asks. He was quite pleased to hear that.

"Leu Motors," Ny replies.

"For real?" Jeff asked Ny in surprise.

"How in the hell did you pull that off? I know a few people that took all those tests, like drug tests and other tests, just to see how smart you are, like math and English. They took their physical and police check and passed on all of them, and they are still on the waiting list." Jeff said in surprise. He couldn't believe what he heard.

"Well, like they say, it's not what you know but who you know. My cousin's husband has an uncle who is the Asst. Manager at Leu Motors, and he pulled me right on in." Ny made up a story and told him. She did not tell him anything about meeting Don and getting a job through him.

"Hey! Do you think you can get me on there?" Jeff asked Ny for a favor.

"Well, let me get my foot in the door good. Then I will see what I can do because I don't know my cousin's husband's uncle. I just met him today when he gave me the job. I think he likes me, and that's why he pulled some strings and got me hired. But if I brought some other man around this quick, he could get me out of there as fast as he brought me in. And that could mess up things for both of us. So I just let him think I'm a little interested until I get into the union. And once I'm in the union, the company can't get rid of me for any reason. So be patient. I got your back." Ny said.

"I heard that! It must help to be a super fine woman and be able to walk thru doors that the average person has slammed in their face." Jeff said.

"Just like they say, you got to use what you got to get what you want," Ny answers him.

"How are you going to get there? That place is way over on the other side of town. It's an hour's drive from here, and catching the bus and the way that they run, hell! It would take you at least two hours to get there." Jeff asks Ni. He couldn't stop talking about her new job.

"I have that worked out. My cousin and her husband just moved into a twobedroom apartment that is 2 miles from the job. They said I could stay with them until I get on my feet." Ny said, telling him about the accommodation she's gonna get with the job.

"That sounds good. Well, I will just have to drive an hour to see you." Jeff said, lifting one of his eyebrows.

"Well, you will only be able to see me on the weekends because my cousin's husband made it clear to me that he doesn't want no men coming over and around his place," Ny said.

"What! What kind of shit is that? I'm coming to see you. Not his wife." Jeff said in an agitated voice.

"Well! Some men are funny like that, and I'm in no position to do anything about it. But I will be in the union in 3 months. I would be locked in at Leu Motors and then be able to get my own place. So just like I said, "Be patient," Ny answered, giggling as she saw the anger on Jeff's face.

"I guess you're right, hell! You can't have everything go the way you want it, besides I have five months left on my lease, and if it wasn't for that, I would move somewhere over there right now." Jeff said.

"Well, in 5 months, we will get a place together," Ny replied, giving him a solution for what to do after his lease ends.

"Okay, baby, that sounds good," Jeff said in a relieved tone. "So when are you moving in with them?" He continued.

"Friday. I told them I wanted to spend a little time with you since I'm not going to be able to see you the way I would like." Ny said, winking at him.

VI

*N*y's luck is shining all around; within a day or two after being kicked out of Jay's apartment. She now has a job, an apartment, and a sugar daddy. Ny is thrilled that she's landed a job so quickly, especially in a city like New York, where competition is fierce. Her new sugar daddy seems to be well-connected and is showering her with gifts and attention. Ny feels like she's on top of the world and can't believe how everything has fallen into place so easily.

❧ Outside Ny's New Apartment

Ny is standing at the front door as Don pulls up. Don gets out of his car and walks up to Ny, and gives her a kiss. Don hands Ny the keys, and she turns and opens the door. Ny walks in and is surprised to see that the apartment has already been furnished. There is an entertainment center that includes a big screen T.V. in the front room with a sofa, loveseat, chair, and coffee table.

Ny goes into the bedroom, and there is a nice queen size bedroom set with a 36-inch T.V. and clock radio. Ny walks into the kitchen, and everything is new. The stove, frig, microwave, dishwasher, and silverware. Ny is really happy.

"Do all of your apartments look like this?" Ny asked in excitement.

"Hell no! Just for you." Don said, moving closer to Ny.

"Well, I was going to wait a little while and take it slow, but if a man is treating you this good, he has to be rewarded," Ny said in a flirty voice, giving him an addictive look.

Ny takes Don's hand and leads him into the bedroom. Ny is getting undressed, and Don is losing his mind watching her. He is so excited that he is having trouble getting out of his suit. They started making love, and Don didn't last two minutes.

"I can't believe this. No woman ever made me feel this way. I never came that fast, and I have to be honest, you are the best I ever had." Don said. He couldn't forget the feeling of making love with Ny.

Ny is looking at Don, and his expression is like his world just got turned upside down. Ny is smiling. She knows that she has Don right where she wants him.

"This is just the first time. You will last a little longer the next time." Ny said, kissing him on his lips.

"I have to be getting back to work anyway. I would like to see you tonight.

Wait! I can't. I have to take my wife to a party. I hope it doesn't bother you that I'm married?" Don said as he got dressed.

"Yes, it does," Ny replied, making a sad face.

"But why?" Don asked her.

"You and I could never be serious. I might want to be married to you someday." Ny said. She had something on her mind.

"We just met. How could you say that?" Don asked her.

"That's right! We just met and looked at everything you have already done for me, and we just made love, or do you do this kind of thing for every woman you meet?" Ny said.

"You do have a point. The thought never crossed my mind that you would want to marry me." Don said, forced to think that Ny might have a valid point.

"Hell! What woman in her right mind wouldn't? You have a great job, you know how to make money, you know how to treat a woman, and the best thing is that you are a real good lover." Ny said, trying to sound more intense.

"How can you say that? I only lasted 2 minutes." Don asks her. He was quite eager to know why Ny could say that he was perfect marriage material.

"But it was a damn good 2 minutes, and when you get used to me, it will last even longer," Ny replied confidently.

"What about this? You can look at me and tell that I'm almost twice your age." Don asked her.

"Just like wine, it just gets better with time," Ny said. It looked like she had answers to all the questions Don had to ask. Don has a look on his face that shows he can't believe what he is hearing.

"How about we get together tomorrow afternoon?" He asks her.

"Sure, how about some shopping? Will you take me?" Ny asked him with a smile.

"I can't be seen in public like that, but how about I come over, and we spend a little time together, and I will give you a few hundred dollars, and you can go and get whatever it is you want?" He said.

"That sounds good," Ny replies.

"Okay! I will call you when I'm on my way." Don said.

"How are you going to call me? I don't have a phone." Ny replies sadly.

Don smirked and said, "Oh yes, you do. Don hands her a cell phone"

Ny sees the phone. She picks up the phone, and there is a dial tone. She runs back to where Don is standing and gives him a kiss and a hug.

"No man has ever treated me this good, and you think I wouldn't want to be married to a man like you? Please! In a heartbeat." She said while hugging Don.

That statement really has Don thinking. Don pulls a piece of paper out of his back pocket and starts writing.

"Here is your phone number, and I will call you tomorrow to let you know what time I will be here," Don said, handing the number to her.

"Looking forward to it, and thank you for everything," Ny said with a cute smile covering her face.

Don leaves, and Ny gets right on the phone.

"Hello! May I speak to Jasmin?" Ny said after dialing a number on her phone.

"Ni! Is this you, girl?" Jasmin asked in excitement.

"It sure is," Ny replies "Girl! I came by your place, and Jay told me he thru your ass out because he caught you fucking some other man that you said was your cousin." Jasmin told her.

"Yeah! It's true!" Ny replied, rolling her eyes out of frustration.

"What in the hell are you doing fucking your own cousin?" Jasmin asked in disbelief.

"No, dumb ass! It was Jeff. Somehow he found out about him coming over, and I told Jay that Jeff was my cousin." Ny told her that she had lied to Jay about Jeff being her cousin.

"So where are you now? Staying with Jeff?" Jasmin asked. She was curious about where Ny was staying now.

"I was up until today," Ny said.

"What happened? Did he catch you fucking somebody else too?" Jasmin asked.

"Naw, girl! You ain't gonna believe this shit here I'm about to tell you." Ny said. She was too excited to tell Jasmin all about her job and stuff.

"Talk to me!" Jasmin said. She was now too excited to know what Ny had to say.

"Last Monday, I was standing at the bus stop, and this old sugar daddy pulled up, driving a nice ride and well dressed. He offered me a ride, but I told him I couldn't go because I was job hunting. He told me it was my lucky day because he is the Asst. Manager at Leu Motors. He took me there, and they hired me on the spot, and I start Monday." She tells Jasmin all about Don and how she met him.

"You have got to be bullshiten!" Jasmin exclaimed. She couldn't believe what Ny just told her.

"Oh, it gets better. Listen to this. This old mother fucker got money like it ain't shit!

Do you hear me? He owns some apartments 2 miles from the job and lets me stay here rent-free, plus he furnished it with all new stuff. I got one of them big screen TVs, and he gave me the phone I'm talking on ready to go." Ny continued with excitement. She couldn't believe what just happened to her here.

"I'm jealous! How often do you think you have to fuck his old ass." Jasmin said.

"I don't know. Maybe once or twice a week. And that ain't gonna be no big deal because I just gave him some pussy, and his old ass said he was sorry that he couldn't last more than two minutes. But the truth be told, he was gone in 30 seconds and just rolled around for the other minute and a half. HA! HA! Besides, he's married, so you know he has to go home to his wife." Ny said, making fun of him, rolling to the ground.

"Yea! What you say is all true in all, but! If he's doing all of those things for you? You may have to put out a little more than that." Jasmin said.

"I can see it in his face Jasmin. I got this old mother fucker right where I want him. I got his old ass thinking I would marry him if he wasn't already married. And as long as he is thinking like that? He ain't gonna make too many waves." Ny replied.

She had a clear idea of what Don wanted from here.

"You just might be right! Hey! Let's go out and kick it, girl; plus, I got to come by and check out your new place. Give me your new phone number so I can call you when I'm on the way." Jasmin replied, giggling.

"Okay! Hold on for a minute. I have to find that piece of paper he wrote it on." Ny said.

Ny looks around for the number, and she sees the paper on the coffee table.

She picks it up and realizes that it is a bank statement, and she turns it over, and her number is on there. She starts walking towards the phone; then she stops dead in her tracks. Ny looks at the other side of the paper and then starts screaming. Ny runs and picks up the phone.

"Are you alright?" Jasmin asked. She was terrified by her scream.

"You are not going to believe this. But that old mother fucker wrote my number on the back of his bank statement, and it says he has $225,000.00 in the bank." Ny exclaimed. She couldn't believe what she just saw.

"You're lying!" Jasmin asked, his eyes popping out of excitement. She couldn't believe what she just saw.

"I will show you when you come over tonight. He is supposed to give me some money to go shopping tomorrow. I ought to make his old ass buy me a car." Ny said she could see all her dreams coming true.

"Just take it slow, girl. If he is doing all of these things for you, believe me, you got that coming too. So I will see you tonight, around 9 or 9:30. Goodbye."

Jasmin tried to warn Ni.

VII

❧ Monday-Inside Leu Motors

*N*y and a group of other people that are hired with her are touring the plant.

Almost every man stops what he is doing to take a look at Ni. Some of them have missed parts of their job from looking too hard at Ni. You can hear the supervisor yelling at the men to get back to work and stop looking at that woman. A big smile came on Ni's face when she heard that.

"Man! Do you see that fine-ass woman right there? I am going to have to get me some of that." One worker said to his fellow co-worker.

"Not before I do!" The other worker replied.

Ny pretended not to hear their crude remarks and just continued to follow the group on tour. She knew she had the power to make men drool over her, and she enjoyed the attention. As the tour continued, the supervisor noticed that Ny was not paying attention to what he was saying, and he asked her a question. Ny quickly replied with a vague answer, causing the supervisor to give her a stern look.

After the tour was over, Ny went to her work station feeling confident and in control. She knew she had the attention of her male co-workers, and she couldn't wait to use it to her advantage. She was determined to climb the corporate ladder and become the boss of the company one day. And with her looks and charm, she knew she could make it happen.

❧   Inside Ni's Apartment

Ny is watching T.V., and there is a knock on the door. Ny gets up and walks up and the door, wondering who could be visiting her at this time. As she opened the door, she saw Jasmin, her best friend, standing there with a smile on her face.

"What's up, girl? Come on in." Ny answered.

"I was in the hood and thought I would stop by and see how your first day at work was?" Jasmin said, with a wide smile on her face.

"Today was just orientation. But I will be on that line tomorrow night." Ny answered.

"Have you heard from Jeff?" Jasmin asked her, reminding her about Jeff.

"I haven't given him a second thought until you just mentioned his name," Ny said.

"So! Does that mean you're not going to see him anymore?" Jasmin questioned her.

"What in the hell for? He can't come over here, and I'm not going back over in that trash can. Now that I'm working at Leu, there are some tricks in their girl.

Just about every man in there was watching every move I made. These dudes are making top dollar, so why would I want to be bothered with Jeff's broke ass. He was good for the time, but now it is time to move on." Ny replied. She was in no mood to greet her torn old life. She was quite happy with all that she had at that time.

"I feel ya! Well, let me get my ass on up out of here. I'll holler at ya! Jasmin said, giggling.

Jasmin leaves, and the phone rings. Ny answers it, and it's her mother.

"Hello, Ny! Your father and I are on our way to come and see you. Everybody in the family is so proud of you for getting that good job at Leu, and please don't mess it up by dealing with the men that work there. Just go to work and do what you're supposed to do and leave those men alone." Mrs. Baker said.

Ny's heart raced with excitement as she heard her mother's voice on the other end of the phone. She hadn't seen her parents in months, and the thought of their visit filled her with joy. Her mother informed her that they were on their way to visit her.

"Okay, mama! I see you and dad when you all get here." Ny said and hung up the call.

Mr. and Mrs. Baker come walking thru the front door, and they have Ni's younger brothers with them, Billy and Gary, who are now young men. Mr. and Mrs. Baker see all the new furniture, big screen T.V., and appliances; they stop and look at each other and then look at Ny with small frowns on their faces. Billy and Gary can't believe what they are looking at.

"Damn, sis! How did you get all of this so fast?" Gary asked her sister.

"I'm hip! Hey! When can I bring some of my women over here?" Billy asked, looking at Ni.

"Ni! Your father and I want to talk to you privately in your bedroom." Mrs. Baker said, hesitating.

They all walk inside Ni's bedroom and shut the door. Mr. Baker was quite frustrated with Ni.

"Ni! And I do mean this! And don't you lie to me? How in the hell did you get all of this when you haven't worked a job in months." Mr. Baker said angrily, pointing his finger at Ni.

"The man who got me hired is renting me this apartment for $900.00 a month.

When he gave me the keys, all of this stuff was already in here." Ny replied in a convincing tone.

"I have heard of furnished apartments before, but ain't nobody furnishing anything like this. Big screen T.V. and get your phone on too.

Are you doing anything with this man?" Mrs. Baker said. She wasn't sure that Ny was being honest this time.

"Nothing! He is married, and he looks like he is older than daddy." Ny replied.

"Well, that explains it. The older man wants a pretty young girl on the side.

As your mother, I'm going to tell you to please do not get involved with a married man. I know you are a grown woman, and I'm not trying to treat you like a child, but some of these women will kill over their husbands, especially if they think he's giving his money away too some young ass woman and not to her." Mrs. Baker said.

She was quite confident that Ny was just as she was in the old days.

"Your mother is right! It's not worth it. And before you can say it, I'm going to tell you. If he acts like he doesn't want anything from you now, he will later, and you can believe that." Mr. Baker agreed with his wife.

"Don't worry! I have it under control." Ny said. She was now getting bored of all the discussion.

The Baker family leaves and gets into their car. Mr. Baker is shaking his head.

"What's wrong with you, Joe?" Mrs. Baker said, looking at her tensed husband.

"One day, that girl is going to get herself in a world of trouble, and there won't be anybody there to help her, not even us." Mr. Baker replied in a worried tone.

"We did all that we could do for her. Now the only thing we can do is pray that nothing happens to her." Mrs. Baker said, consoling her husband.

❧ Inside Leu Motors-Cafe

Ny is having lunch, and a man who works there pulls up a seat next to her. Ny finds the man attractive, and she starts smiling at him.

"Hello! My name is Nick, and yours?" Nick said.

"My name's Ny!" Ny replies.

"I've never seen you before. How long have you been working here." Nick tries to flirt with her.

"Almost a month," Ny replied after calculating her working days.

"I just came back to nights because I was offered a better job than what I was doing on days. So how is everyone treating you so far?" Nick asked her.

"Well, some of the women here act as if they hate on me, and half of the men are trying to give me their phone numbers, but for the most part, it's okay because I'm here for one thing and one thing only and I don't have to tell you what that is," Ny answered sternly.

"Hey! You and me both! It was nice meeting you, Ny. Hope to see you around sometimes." Nick replied.

Ny said goodbye, and she was impressed with Nick because he was one of the few men that came up to her without trying to hit on her.

❧ Outside Of Leu Motors – 2 Weeks Later

It's the end of the shift, and Ny is waiting on a taxi because the buses don't run that late at night. Ny feels a tap on her back, and she turns around, and it's Nick.

"How are you doing? Haven't seen you around for a few days." Nick asks her.

"I have been here, but you know how big this place is," Ny said.

"I noticed that you have been catching a cab sometimes when we get off from work. Is that what you are waiting on now?" Nick asked her, as he had usually seen her getting a cab back home.

"It sure is," Ny replied.

"How would you like to save your money and let me drop you off?" Nick said, offering her a lift back home.

Ny starts thinking about it because she is worried about what Don would think about her riding around with another man that works for Leu, especially when Don is giving her the cab fare. Ny looks up at Nick, and she likes him more now than she did before.

"Okay! Why not?" Ny said and sat in his car.

Inside Nick's Car Ny is truly impressed with the car he is driving. Ny is giving him directions on where she lives.

"You hungry, because if you are? There is a place called Sammy's, and they have the best food in the world." Nick asks her as he is starving.

Ny is starting to fall for Nick, and for a few moments, she isn't thinking about Don. When Don did come to her mind, she thought about him being on days and she on nights, and nobody really knows her and sure as hell can't connect her with Don, so Ny starts thinking, why not?

"Alright! You talk me into it. Let's go." Ny said as she, too, was hungry.

Nick pulls up to Sammy's and opens the car door for Ni, letting her out first before heading towards the restaurant. The place was packed with people, and the smell of fresh food was intoxicating. Nick and Ny managed to grab a booth and started looking over the menu.

"What do you recommend?" Ny asked Nick.

Nick looked at the menu for a few seconds and then pointed to a dish, "I would recommend the chicken parmesan. It's the best thing they have here."

Ny agreed with Nick and ordered the same thing. As they waited for their food, they chatted about their jobs and personal lives. Ny found herself opening up to Nick and telling him about her recent breakup with Jay.

"That guy didn't deserve you anyway," Nick said as he took a sip of his drink.

Ny smiled at him and felt a sense of comfort. Maybe Nick was right. Jay wasn't the right guy for her. She was just using him as a safety net.

Their food arrived, and they started eating. The chicken parmesan was amazing, just as Nick had promised. Ny was enjoying the food and the company, and for the first time in a while, she felt happy.

As they finished their meal, Nick paid the bill, and they walked back to his car. Ny couldn't help but feel grateful for Nick's kindness and company. They exchanged numbers and promised to keep in touch.

As Ny got out of Nick's car and headed towards her apartment, she couldn't shake off the feeling that something was about to change in her life. She just didn't know what it was yet.

❧ Outside Ni's Apartment –

Nick and Ny are pulling up "Thank you for a wonderful meal," Ny said. She had a great time after a very long time.

"You are more than welcome. Maybe we can do this again sometime? Wait a minute! How rude of me. I never asked if you had a man?" Nick said. He was quite eager to know whether Ny was dating someone or not.

"No, I don't have a man, but I am seeing someone, and he is paying for me to stay in this apartment and is taking care of allot of things I need," Ny said. For the first time in her life, she had been honest with a man.

"I understand. You have a married sugar daddy," Nick said. After a pause and looking closely at each other, both of them burst into laughter.

"You catch on real quick," Ny said. She smiled, feeling relieved that Nick was understanding of her situation. She had been afraid he might judge her for being involved with a married man.

"Thanks, Nick. I appreciate that," Ny said. "And I had a great time with you too."

"So, if someone is taking care of you like that, we all know that you can't take a chance on messing that up. Ni, I must say I really enjoyed your company, and I will see you around the plant." Nick just as Ny was about to step out of the car.

"Nick! I never said I wouldn't go out with you again. I just told you what's going on with me, and if you can deal with that, then we have no problem. That is, if you can keep your mouth shut. I want nobody to know my business. You never know who knows who." Ny said, with sadness in her voice.

"Not only that's no problem, but I also know how to keep my mouth shut," Nick said confidently. He took Ny in confidence that her secret was safe with him.

"I have enough guys jealous of me as it is. If they found out that I was seeing you, they would really hate me then," Ny said.

Ny got out of the car and waved goodbye as Nick drove off. She felt a mix of excitement and guilt, but she couldn't deny that she was looking forward to seeing him again. However, she knew that she needed to be careful and keep her secret life hidden from everyone, including Nick

VII

1 Week Later Ny and Nick had been dating for a week now, and they had a strong connection. They had a lot of fun together and enjoyed each other's company. Ny and Nick are riding in his car, and Nick is going is usual route, then Ny stops him.

"Since we don't have to work tomorrow, how about we go have a drink somewhere instead of going out to eat?" Ny asked him. She wanted to have some fun with him.

"Sounds good to me, and I know the place to go," Nick replied and agreed to Ni's suggestion.

It's about 3:00 am, and Ny and Nick are leaving the bar. They hop in Nick's car and pull off.

"I really had a good time, so good that I'm not ready for the night to end," Ny said. She was very happy and felt quite lively.

"Well, would you like to come over to my house for a few drinks and play some pool with me?" Nick invited her to his home for some games and more drinks.

"Sure! I want to see how you live anyway."

Ny and Nick's relationship had become quite intimate, with them making love almost every other night. They had a deep physical connection, but they also cared about each other on a deeper level.

ꙮ Outside Of Nick's House –

Ny is really impressed when they pull up in his driveway. Nick and Ny arrive at Nick's house, and it's a beautiful home with a swimming pool and a nice view of the city.

"Wow! You have a beautiful home. Show it to me." Ny said she was quite impressed by Nick's home. It was grand and luxurious.

Nick takes her on a tour of the house, and the last room he shows her is his bedroom. When Ny sees the bed, she jumps right into it.

"Nick, I hope you don't mind if I don't want to play pool. Now that I see this bed and lay in it, I realize that I am tired. Can I lay here for a few minutes?" Ny said.

Ny starts twisting and turning around like she is trying to get comfortable and making sexual moves by touching herself and sticking her butt up in the air but is playing it off like she is half asleep. Nick is watching her body movements and can't take his eyes off her.

"You can spend the night if you want to?" Nick said, looking at him with passion.

"Well, let me get comfortable," Ny said in a seductive voice. With this, she starts undressing herself.

"What would you like to sleep in? A T-shirt or P.J. top." Nick said.

"Nothing!" Ny replied.

"You're just like me. I don't sleep in anything either," Nick said and jumped up into the bed.

Nick didn't waste any time getting undressed and hopping on top of Ny . After they were finished, they took a shower together, Nick changed the sheets, and then they went to sleep.

Ny woke up in the morning and looked at the clock. It struck 11:37 am. Ny lays back down, then jumps right back up in a panic. She shakes Nick until he wakes up. Ny jumps out of bed and puts her clothes back on, and rushes Nick to do the same.

"I'm supposed to meet sugar daddy at my apartment at Noon," Ny said. She was panicked at the thought that she might get late and get caught.

"Okay, I'm ready. We got about 12 minutes to get you back there, and we may be five or ten minutes late, depending on lights and traffic." Nick said and immediately hopped out of bed.

It's 12:06 pm, and Ny sees Don's car parked in front of her apartment. She tells Nick to keep going and drop her off at the corner store. Ny gets out in a hurry and runs into the store without saying goodbye to Nick. Ny buys a few items and walks back to her apartment. Don is sitting in the car waiting on her. Ny is scared because she doesn't know how long he's been there, and she thinking of a good lie to tell him.

"Hello, baby! Have you been waiting long?" Ny asked Don.

"Yes, I have! And where have you been? I told you I was going to be here at 10:30 am. Now look at what time it is. You're almost 2 hours late; what happened?"

Don replied he was in a terrible mood. He had been waiting for her for more than 30 minutes now.

"I'm sorry! I thought you said noon." Ny said, making a sad face.

"That was last week. So where have you been?" Don asked her sternly, lifting one of his eyebrows.

"I spent the night with my girl Jasmin. She picked me up from work last night and wanted me to go out and have a drink with her. She ended up having one drink after another one, and she became too drunk to drive, so I ended up sleeping over there." Ny told Don. Her heart almost skipped a beat.

"How come you didn't drive and let her spend the night over here?" He asked.

"I thought about that, but Jasmin's car is in the shop, and she was driving her boyfriend's car, and it is a stick, and I don't know how to drive one of those. But if I had my own car, I could have come home and not be at the mercy of other people." Ny said, trying her best to let the story sound natural.

"That's the very reason I wanted you to be here at 10:30 am so we could go to the car auction, which starts at 11:00 am. But we still have time before they close at 2:00 pm, so get in. The only thing is that most of the good cars are gone early, and they only have this every six months. Oh, by the way, I see you have on your Leu uniform, and that's good. So if I see someone I know, I'm here on business with one of my employees." Don said he was taking her to the car auction.

꙰ Inside The Car Auctions

Ny and Don are walking in. Ny sees what she wants immediately. It's a Conv. Mustang and the bidding price started off at $5,000.00

Ny tells Don that is what she wants. The auctioneer is now asking for $6,000.00, and somebody raised their hand, and now he is asking for $7,000.00, and Don raised his hand. The Auctioneer is now asking for $8,000.00, and no one raised their hand. So the Auctioneer asked for $7,500.00, and someone raised their hand, and this pissed Don off.

"What in the hell is he doing? He is supposed to go, going once, going twice, and sold! He's is not supposed to go down in price!" Don said he was now agitated with the price increasing every 2 minutes.

The auctioneer is now asking for $8,000.00, and Ny is pulling on Don to get this car. Don looks at Ny, then raises his hand. The Auctioneer is now asking for $8,500.00, and no one raised their hand.

"$8,000.00 going once, going twice, sold to the man in the blue suit." The auctioneer said, looking to see if any other person was up for the same car too.

Ny is jumping up and down and spinning around. Don goes over to look at the car and make sure everything is alright. He walks around the car and likes what he sees. He looks inside, and all of a sudden, a puzzled look comes on his face. Don gets Ni's attention and motions her to come to where he's at.

"I'm sorry, Ny, but we can't get this car," Don said as he found that something was not right with the car.

"What! What do you mean? Why not?" Ny said, and her smile started fading away.

"Look inside," Don said, pointing toward the car.

Ny looks inside and sees that it is a stick shift. Ny looks hard at Don, then grabs him and starts begging him to buy the car.

"Come on, baby. Please buy this one for me. I am a fast learner. I know I will be able to do it. Come on, baby; please buy this car for me?" Ny begged Don. She desperately wanted that car.

"I don't know, Ni?" Don replied. He wasn't sure whether to get that car or not.

Don shakes his head, and Ny starts sobbing. Don sees Ny crying, and it gets to him.

"Okay! Okay! Stop crying. I will get the car. But how are we going to get it back to your place? I can't drive two cars at the same time, and I can't take a chance on anyone seeing you driving my car." Don said as he saw her crying.

"There is a big parking lot next door to this place. Take me over there so I can practice." Ny said, making an innocent face and gazing at him.

Ny is behind the wheel, and Don is showing her what to do. In about ten minutes, Ny had the stick-down pack. Don was impressed.

"Hey! I think you're ready. I follow behind you just in case you have some problems." Don said.

"Okay! And when we get back home, I'm going to show you just how much I love what you do for me. I love you, Don!" Ny said in excitement. She always wanted to get a car, and now finally, she has one.

Don is driving down the street. He just left Ni's place, and his car phone rang.

Don picks it up, and it is his wife. Don hears her voice, and it makes his flesh crawl.

Don has fallen so much in love with Ny to the point that now he can't stand his wife.

"Hey, there, honey! I have been looking for you." Don's wife said as soon as Don received the call.

"What! I'm busy. I told you I had to come in to work and take care of some contracts, so what in the hell are you looking for? Is it important? If not? Stop calling me so much! Okay! Alright! Goodbye!" Don angrily said and hung up the call.

Don's wife looks at the phone and then hangs it up. She has a sad look on her face. After getting into a relationship with Ni, Don becomes distant and cold toward his wife, blaming her for every little thing that went wrong in their lives. She couldn't help but wonder if he had fallen out of love with her, or worse, if he had fallen for some other woman.

As for Don, little did he know that Ny had no intention of marrying him or being with him long-term. She was just using him for his money and the lavish lifestyle he provided her.

Inside Ni's Apartment Ny is sitting on her sofa talking on the phone to Jasmin.

"Hey Jasmin! I got that old mother fucker to buy me a car." Ny said, flexing her car and smiling her heart out.

"No shit! What kind?" Jasmin said. She was shocked to see Ny with a car. So, Ny finally got what she said.

"A 1986 Conv. Mustang." Ny replied. She was damn excited to drive that car along the road.

"Girl, you must be really putting it on him," Jasmin said.

"Yea! I got him thinking he is a really good lover. Just like today, he was happy that he lasted 3 minutes, and I told him that I was watching the clock and it was 5 minutes, and no man ever made me have an organism in 5 minutes." Ny replied. She had already made up her mind to get a car from Don, and yet she did.

"What stupid person said you don't get to be old being no fool? Because it sounds like you got an old fool. What do you think, Ny? Is he in love, or is he dumb?"Jasmin said and started laughing.

"He is both! Remember this? Love will make you dumb. Oh yea! I lied to you, Don. I spent the night with that guy Nick I was telling you about. I didn't get up in time, and Don was here waiting. I told him that I spent the night with you, so if it ever comes up? Please remember. Okay!" Ny said, giggling. It was all going according to her plan.

"I got your back," Jasmin said.

As Ny spoke to Jasmin, she couldn't help but share the details of her latest conquest with Don. She boasted about how she had manipulated him into buying her an expensive car worth a whopping 8,000 dollars. Jasmin listened, somewhat shocked, as Ny continued to go on and on about how easy it was to get Don to do whatever she wanted. It was clear that Ny had no intention of being faithful to Don and was simply using him for his money and his physical affection.

Jasmin, who had always been a good friend to Ni, tried to reason with her, telling her that she was playing with fire and that it was only a matter of time before everything blew up in her face. But Ny just brushed it off, insisting that she knew what she was doing and that she was in control of the situation. Deep down, however, she couldn't help but wonder if Jasmin was right. Was she really in control, or was she playing a dangerous game that could end in disaster?

IX

❧ 6 Months Later-Inside Nick's House

*N*y and Nick are lying in bed. Ny and Nick were lying in bed, facing each other. The room was quiet except for the occasional sound of cars passing by outside.

Nick reached out and started playing with Ni's hair, twirling it between his fingers.

She smiled at him, feeling content and loved.

"You know, I never get tired of looking at you," Nick said, his eyes tracing the curves of Ni's face.

Ny blushed, feeling a warmth spread through her body. "You always know how to make me feel special," she replied.

Nick leaned in and kissed her gently on the lips. As they pulled away, he looked into her eyes and said, "I love you, Ni. I hope you know that."

Ny felt her heart skip a beat. She knew she loved Nick too, but saying it out loud always made her feel vulnerable. "I love you too, Nick," she whispered, snuggling closer to him.

They lay in silence for a while, enjoying each other's company. Ny couldn't help but feel grateful for having someone like Nick in her life. As they were lying there in peace, Nick remembered something he heard at work.

"Ni, did you hear about the new plant Leu Motors built in Kansas City?" Nick said, being playful with her hair.

"Yeah, I did. I also heard that the company is going to give $25,000.00 to anyone who goes there to work." Ny replied.

"Well, I'm selling my house, and I am going. But the most important thing is that you come with me. What I am asking you, Ny, is that will you marry me? Just think about all of the things we could have together. The cost of living down there is dirt cheap. For what I paid for this house? We could go down there and get one in a great neighborhood that is three times the size of this one, and they come with big backyards and basements. Let me see your hand Ny so I can put this ring on your finger."

Ny is shocked by what he just said. Without wasting a single second, Ny replies, "Yes, Nick. I will marry you. But now I got to find a way of getting rid of Don. Do you think you have enough room to put whatever I have in my apartment in your basement?

"Yes, of course!" Nick replied.

"Okay, because today is Monday, and we are not going to work on Wednesday. That is going to be the day I move. Give us time to rent a truck and get people to help us move." Ny explained to him. She was quite interested in him too.

"Why can't we just hire some movers?" Nick asked her.

"Did you forget that ain't nothing in that apartment is mined? Do you think that Don would let me have all that stuff when I tell him that I'm going to marry you when he is thinking that I'm going to marry him? Now here is the plan. It is cold outside, so the movers can wear ski masks, and won't nobody gets suspicious. After we get everything out of the apartment and into your house, then I am going to call Don and tell him that some men have kicked the door in and stole everything out of the apartment and raped me." Ny told Nick about the evil plan to get rid of Don.

"Are you sure this is going to work? You know the first thing Don is going to do is call the police. Then the police are going to find out who rented moving trucks that day, and it will eventually lead to us." Nick asked. He wasn't sure this plan would work out for them. Nick was scared that Don might involve the cops and they might get into some deep trouble.

"No, it won't. I will have my brother Gary go rent it with one of his fake credit card IDs with a different name on it. They will be out there looking for somebody that doesn't exist. Ny said with a wicked smile on her face.

Nick was quite impressed by Ni's idea and said in surprise, "I must admit, you just may have something here, but one thing I want to tell you, and that is, you just didn't think up all of this right off the top of your head right now. How long have you been planning this?"

"A long time. My problem was finding somewhere to put it. But now we are going to get married and move to St. Louis. That problem is solved. I have been thinking of a way to get away from him after he bought me that car." Ny told him. She was all set to get rid of Don and begin a new life with Nick.

"You said he put the car in your name. Why didn't you just pack your bags and come live with me? I have been asking you to do that for the last 3 or 4 months." Nick asked her. He still wasn't confident about the plan so far.

"Let me put it to you like this. First of all, I didn't know how serious you were until you put that big ass rock on my finger. Secondly, you have no idea of what it is like to have an out-of-shape, smelly old bastard like that on top of you once or twice a week. While I was going thru that shit, I made up my mind when I did leave;

I'm taking everything in that apartment with me because I earned it. Now if there are no more questions, just be ready to move Wednesday, and remember, when that day comes, I will be yours and only yours forever. You are my dream come true, and I really do love you, Nick." Ny said out of frustration. She hated Don and was with him because of the thousands of bucks he had in his bank account. Now that Nick had proposed to her, she could easily kiss his ass and live with someone she actually loved.

"I love you too!" Nick replied.

With the plan set in motion, Ny was eager to leave Don behind and start a new life with Nick. She had it all planned out, and with Nick by her side, she felt confident that everything would work out. As Wednesday approached, Ny couldn't wait to leave everything behind and begin a new chapter in her life. She had chosen Nick over Don, and with the ring on her finger, she knew that she was making the right decision. Little did she know, things were about to take a turn she never expected.

❧ Wednesday- Outside Ni's Apartment

It's 15 degrees outside, and all of the movers have on ski masks and gloves.

The truck is loaded with everything, including the dishwasher and kitchen sink. Nick is ready to get in the truck and leave. Ny calls him back into her bedroom.

"What do you want? We need to get out of here." Nick said, reminding her that he had to leave the place as soon as possible.

"Look here, dumb ass! I have been raped! Remember, Don is going to call the police when he sees that all of his shit is gone. Now they are going to take me to the hospital and examine me, so it has to look like I have been raped. Then I can tell Don that I need to take a leave of absence from work, and I'm going back home to live with my parents, where I feel safe. Don knows that he can't call or come over to my parent's house because he is married. When you and I get settled in KC next month, I will call him and let him know that I took the transfer because I wanted a different environment because of what happened to me, and I didn't want to be in New York anymore. Doing it like this, he would never suspect that I left his ass and ripped him off at the same time. So now, please! Come over here and fuck me!" Ny said, reminding him of the moves to make the plan look real.

Nick is making love to Ni, but he is taking too long to cum. Ny is getting mad.

"Will you please hurry up? Damn! Now is the time I need an old mother fuckin two-minute man." Ny said she was annoyed and wanted Nick to finish quickly.

"Okay, it's coming! There it is." Nick replied, breathing heavily.

"Hit me in the face!" Ny said. She wanted the rape and robbery plan to look real.

"I'm not going to hit you," Nick said, stepping backward.

"Oh, you soft mother fucker! We ain't got time for this shit. Pull out your knife and hand it to me!" Ny said, smiling.

Nick gives Ny the knife, and she presses the blade right on her neck that leaves a print and a small cut. Then she opens the bedroom door, bends her head down, and slams it twice right over the corner of her eye. A knot appears with a little blood.

Nick can't believe what he is seeing.

"Call me as soon as you all get everything in there, so I can remind you to tell my brother Gary to call me from mom's house, so I will know that he dropped off the truck," Ny said, turning to Nick.

"Before I leave, tell me, how do you know you can trust these guys to keep their mouths shut?" Nick asked, as he was quite nervous about the entire plan.

"2 of them are my brothers, 2 of them are my uncles, and the other 3 are my cousins. Now you know, the whole time I was here, I didn't pay rent or bills, so you know I have one hell of a bank account. I paid them really well, so I can spend the rest of my life with your ass. One of my cousins is a carpenter and Plummer, and he costs extra. How in the hell do you think he got that dishwasher and sink out of here so quickly and didn't leave a drop of water? Now will you get the fuck out of here, please?" Ny replied confidently.

Nick kisses Ny goodbye and then leaves. 2 hours later, the phone rings, and it's Nick letting Ny know that everything is in the house and her brother will be calling her soon. Twenty minutes later, Gary called to let her know the truck has been dropped off. Ny gets on the phone and calls Don at work, crying.

"Slow down! I can't understand you." Don said he was terrified to hear Ny crying.

"Some men rushed the door in on me, stole everything out of the apartment, and one of them raped me," Ny said, pretending to cry and breathing heavily. She did her best to let it all sound natural.

When Don heard this, he ran out of Leu Motors, yelling at his Asst. to tell everybody he had an emergency and that he would explain when he got back. Don walks into the apartment to see that everything is gone. He doesn't see Ni, so he yells her name, and she comes running out of the bedroom and jumps into his arms. Don is so sad to see Ny in this shape. Dons sees that she has been struck a couple of times.

"Don't worry! I'm here now! Did you call the police?" Don asked out of care and anger.

"No! I am scared! Embarrassed, and I didn't want anybody to know that this happened to me. I don't want to be on the news or have my name in the paper." Ny said, trying to sound scared and timid.

"Don't worry about that. The police will keep it confidential if that's what you want. I'm getting ready to call them right now." Don said, holding her hand and consoling her.

Don calls the police and tells Ny he is going to use the bathroom. Don lets out a yell! Saying, damn! These clowns even took the toilet. Ny didn't know that they took the toilet, but when she heard Don say that, she really started crying real tears from laughter. Don came out of the bathroom bitching about the toilet, and it was making Ny laugh harder.

Ny covers up her laughter by screaming and hollering. Don tries to pick Ny up, but she is lying face down on the floor, and she pulls away from him so he will not see her face. Ny lays like that for a minute until the laughter is gone, and then she raises up with her hands covering her face. Don removes Ny's hands from her face, and Don sees more tears on Ny's face, more than before. Ny has a really sad look on her face, and Don is really feeling sorry for her.

"I am going to do all I can to find out who did this to you," Don said. He was filled with anger and wanted to kill them all.

Don gives Ny a hug. There is a knock on the door, and it's the police. Don is telling them what happened. One of the Policemen helps Ny up and walks her into the ambulance.

X

❧ Inside The Hospital-Examination Room

*T*he hospital room was quiet as Ny sat on the edge of the examination table, still in shock from the traumatic experience she had just endured. It had all started with a planned robbery at her apartment, or so she thought. Ny had reported the incident to the police, but now, as a detective stood before her, she was scared that the truth might come out.

A doctor hands a detective a medical report, and it says that the victim has semen inside and outside her body, and they conclude that the woman was beaten and raped. The detective walks up to Ny and asks her a few questions. Ny nods her head yes.

The detective began by telling Ny the results of the medical report, that she had been sexually assaulted and beaten. Ny was already aware of it all because she was the one who had planned it. She knew she had to come clean, but the words caught in her throat. Finally, she nodded her head, indicating that she was ready to answer the detective's questions.

"Please start from the beginning and tell me what happened." The detective asked Ni politely.

"I heard a knock on the door. I asked who it was. One of them said," It's the mailman, and we have a package that needs your signature. So I thought nothing of it, and when I opened the door, they just rushed in. It had to be 6, 7, 8, or maybe 9 of them. It happened so fast that before I knew it, they had put me inside the bathtub and told me not to bring my ass out of there unless I wanted to die. They closed the bathroom door, and all I could hear was the furniture moving around." Ny said, telling him the story that she made up to tell the police. Ny had planned every move perfectly. There was no loophole, and now was the time she was executing the act.

"Did you see what any of them look like?" Detective asked Ni.

"They all had on ski masks," Ny replied, with tears filled in her eyes.

"Did you notice any rings or tattoos on their hands or wrist?" The detective asked, trying to gather as many clues as possible to catch the culprits.

"Now that you mention it. I think that they all were wearing gloves." Ny said, pretending to think about their appearance.

"What about their voices? Did they sound black, white, Latin?" The detective asked Ni.

"Like I said, they closed the door on me, and I only heard furniture moving around. Even the guy who raped me didn't say much." Ny replied. She was now getting annoyed by the interrogation.

"Tell me about that?" The detective asked. He was noting it all down for further investigation.

"The one who raped me came busting thru the bathroom door. Grabbed me out of the tub and rushed me into my bedroom. I tried to resist, and he slammed my head into the edge of the bedroom door. He threw me down on the floor, and as I looked around, I noticed that everything was gone. He pulled out a knife and held it to my neck. Then he said," If you try anything? I will cut your throat." Then he raped me. I couldn't tell you if he sounded black or white or if he had an accent. He also said, "If I come out of this room any time soon, he will kill me" So I stayed balled up in a corner for I don't know how long. The only thing that kept going thru my mind was that I couldn't believe that this had happened to me. When I finally got the courage to open up the door and look out, they were gone, and so was everything else. They even took the dishwasher and the kitchen sink. The only thing they left was the carpet and the drywall." Ny said, sniffing.

"From start to finished, how long would you say it took them?" The detective questioned her, nodding his head in despair.

"If I had to guess, maybe an hour or less," Ny replied.

"The man that raped you? Do you remember the color of his eyes, and were you able to see any skin tone underneath the mask?" The detective asked, trying to get a close detail of the rapist.

"His eyes could have been black or dark brown. His skin tone looks like a light skin black man, a white man with a tan, or Latino. I do remember that he had red lips and yellow teeth." Ny answered, trying to show that she wasn't sure and everything was blacked out when she was getting raped.

"Any golds in his mouth?" The detective asked her.

"If there were, his teeth were so yellow I wouldn't be able to tell," Ny replied.

"Thank you, Ms. Baker, you have been very helpful, and I know this was hard for you to re-live this time in your life. We will keep in touch." The detective said as he asked all the questions from her.

The detective leaves the room and enters the hallway, where another detective is waiting for him.

"So, what do you think?" The other detective asked his fellow detective.

"First, let's find the landlord, and I want you to read this medical report and my notes from the interview with Ms. Baker. After we question the landlord, then we will compare notes. Oh! There he is in the waiting room. Mr. Greybrook, this is my partner Detective Henderson. I just finished talking to Ms. Baker, and we would like to ask you a few questions." The first detective said.

"Go right ahead," Don said.

"How long has Ms. Baker been renting from you?" Detective 1 asked as he started interrogating Don.

"Um 8 months. I guess!" Don replied.

"How did you all meet?" The detective asked him.

"I kind of bumped into her, and she told me that she was job hunting. I am the Asst. Plant Manager at Leu Motors, and she seemed like a nice girl, so I gave her a shot, and she hasn't missed not one day of work." Don replied, telling the detective about how they met each other the very first time.

"I am looking at a report that you gave to Detective Jones, and it's a list of everything that was stolen. How did you know what was in her apartment?" The detective asked Don. He was unable to figure out why a landlord had a detailed list of the furniture and other things present in Ni's apartment.

"Because I furnished everything in there, and all of it was brand new. I still have the receipts to prove it. Thank goodness for insurance." Don answered, clearing all the questions arising in the detective's mind.

"Looking at this report of what was taken, you had some expensive stuff in there. Big screen TVs and leather living room suits, among other things. Do you furnish all of your apartments like this?" Detective 1 continues.

"Look, detective, you are a man just like I am. I saw that pretty, sexy woman, and I did any and everything I could to try and impress her. Please, could this last statement be off the recorder? I am a married man." Don said, telling him that Ny attracted him.

"Yes, it will be off the recorder, and thank you for your time," Detective replied with a smirk.

Don leaves, and so do the detectives. The detectives are inside the police station.

"This is an inside job. The question is? Did she rip him off, or is he trying to rip off the insurance company? I mean, it's just too damn convenient. It's one the coldest day of the year, and nobody is going to give a second thought to guys moving furniture in ski masks and gloves." Detective 2 said he was quite skeptical about the statement Ny gave. He had a feeling that something somewhere was not right. The case was not what it seemed.

"No robber or burglar is going to take that much time cleaning somebody out like that if they didn't know the situation. Hell! They even took time to take the toilet while the occupant was in there and then raped her. When was the last time you worked a case like that?" He continued.

"Never, now it's a matter of who has the most to gain out of this, and of course, it's the landlord. He steals his own property and makes an insurance claim, but why would he let his people rape his mistress?" Detective 1 said.

"He got her a good job, put her up in an apartment, and furnished it with all of the finer things in life, and you know, with his good-paying job, he was giving her money." Detective 2 said. He knew the case wasn't as simple as it appeared to be.

"I think I see where you are going with this. She has been an occupant for eight months, and you know a pretty, fine woman like that is not paying any rent or bills if she has to deal with an old mother fucker like him. Now she has all of this time to save her money. She has been working at Leu Motors for eight months, and you know all the men want her. I would bet my life that she met some young stud that works there, and she wants to be with him. Ms. Baker has enough money to save and decides it is time to go. She tells him that she is going to be moving out, and he can't take it. He has fallen in love with this woman. He feels used, and now he is going to get back at her and make some money doing it. Trying to make up for the lost money he invested in her. He may have told the guys that if you all want her?

You can have her. By now, he thinks of her as a whore and doesn't care about what happens to her if he can't be with her." Detective 1 said.

"There is one thing that bothers me?" Detective 2 said, picking up Ny's medical report.

"And, what's that?" Detective 1 asked him.

"If they would take time to take the toilet? How come they didn't take her car?

Those Mustangs are high on the chopping block." Detective 2 said, expressing his doubts.

"If the car is registered to Ms. Baker, it wouldn't do him any good because he wouldn't be able to collect on the insurance policy. A man like that is not going to be nickel and dimming with chop blocks. It's too much trouble and not worth the money. But if the car is registered to him and they didn't take it? We may have to take a closer look at Ms. Baker. Tell Detective Jones to find out who that car is registered to and ask him for the list of incoming and outcoming phone calls of Ms.

Baker's residents and bring the report of the question and answers from the neighbors." Detective said.

"Here is the Q&A from the neighbors." Detective Jones said.

Detective 1 is looking over it, and a surprised look comes on his face. He shows it to Detective 2.

"When the neighbor was questioned? All of them said the only male company they had seen come to visit her was an older man driving a late model green Lincoln.

They never saw the car at night, only during the day, around 11:00 am to 1:00 pm.

But this is really interesting here. One neighbor said he used to see her catching the bus during the day up until about 4 or 5 months ago when she got her car. Then another neighbor said," They used to see her getting out of a taxi up until about 5 or 6 months ago. Then it was always some fella dropping her off, but he never came in.

When she got her car, the neighbor said she never saw that fella again, that was dropping her off late at night. But lately, like the last 3 or 4 months, her car was never parked outside at night but would be there in the morning. Maybe she was working the graveyard shift." Detective 1 said, showing the papers to Detective Jones.

"Here are the other things you asked for." Detective Jones said. The detectives are looking everything over.

"Okay! This phone number is registered to Nicolas Hines. He works at Leu Motors and has been there about ten years and is 28 years old." Detective 1 said, pointing out Nick's phone number on Ni's call history.

"Alright! We have our young stud. Now we know what graveyard shift she was working." Said Detective 2.

"Now look at this! The car is registered to a Nigeria Baker, but it was bought at an auction, and guess who paid for it? Detective 1 leaned forward to Detective 2, the name that bought Ny a car from the auction.

"Don Greybrook!" Detective 2 said in disbelief.

"That car cost $8000.00, and he's probably paying the insurance. Now she is leaving him for another man, and he is pissed off. We have motive and reason. Now all we have to do is prove it." Detective 1 said. Everything was crystal clear before him.

"I agree with you, but just being the devil's advocate, what makes you so sure she didn't set this up?" Detective 2 said."Also, Leu Motors is only a mile or two from the apartment. Don is the Asst. Plant Manager. He can come and go as he pleases. Now put yourself in Ms. Baker's shoes, your lock-in at your job, you have all this money in the bank, a late model Conv. Mustang and now a person you really want to be with. Don could show up at any time and see that moving truck. Call the police and have you put in jail, and you lose everything. Who in their right mind is going to take that chance? Would you? But the X factor is, why would she just have to have that toilet? Just say she plans on moving in with the young stud. Looking at this Nicks's guy's address, he lives in a very nice part of town, and I don't think he needs a toilet, but Don could always use the toilet in one of his other apartments." Detective One suggested.

"Remember, I do agree with you." Detective 2 said.

As the investigation progressed, it became increasingly clear that Ny had orchestrated the entire plan to get rid of Don and run away with Nick. The evidence found at the scene of the supposed sexual assault, combined with the medical report presented by the doctor, painted a damning picture of Don's involvement.

Despite Don's claims of innocence, the authorities were convinced that he had acted alone and had planned the robbery to get insurance money. They seized his passport, prevented him from leaving the country, and charged him with theft and insurance fraud.

Meanwhile, Ny and Nick had successfully fled the State and were living together in a remote location, free from the consequences of their actions. Don was left to face the legal system alone, with little hope of proving his innocence. It was a stark reminder of the power of evil and the devastating consequences it can have on innocent lives.

XI

🌿 Inside Nick's House-Bedroom

*N*y and Nick are drinking champagne in bed. Listing to the music and having a good time with each other.

"Here is another toast! We pulled it off! I am so glad you came into my life and took me away from that old funky-ass dog. I just don't know what to do!" Ny said. She was quite happy, thinking that her plan worked out. Little did she know that she was getting herself in some deep trouble.

"I am so glad you came into my life. I have the woman of my dreams, and you're going to be my wife. Here is to St. Louis." Nick said in a tone full of love.

St. Louis, Mo.-5 Years Later-Inside Nick, And Ni's House Nick and Ny are married and have a 4-year-old son named Nicolas Hines Jr.

Nick works the night shift, and Ny works the day shift. Nick is walking around the house looking for Ny. She is nowhere to be found; neither is his son. It's 1:00 am, and Nick is already mad because Ny is not home and is getting madder by the minute.

Nick falls asleep. The opening of the front door wakes him up. Ny comes walking in at 3:47 am.

"Where in the hell have you been? You better not tell me on that gambling boat! And where in the hell is Jr," Nick yelled. He was all red in anger and couldn't control his rage.

"I went out for a few drinks, and Jr. is spending the night with my friend Joyce," Ny replied.

"Look at what time it is. How in the hell are you going to get up and go to work in the morning? You promised me that you were not going to gamble anymore after you lost the $3.500.00 we were supposed to spend on our cruise. That was six months ago, and instead of things getting better, it seems like there getting worse.

You have not been taking care of business. I remember the days you wouldn't miss a day of work even when you were sick. Now you have missed more days in one month than you have missed in the last five years. It's starting to get to the point as if I don't know you anymore. Can I trust you to do the right things? I love you! Please look me in the eyes and tell me if I can trust you?" Nick said. He was quite pissed with Ny.

"Yes, baby, you can trust me," Ny replied.

"I have been hearing rumors that you are out here fucking around on me. Is that true?" Nick asked, lifting one of his eyebrows.

"Who in the hell told you some shit like that? Those guys are telling you that shit is just mad because they ain't getting none of this fat ass, and you are. Don't play!" Ny replied in a fit of rage and threw her bag on the floor.

"Okay! I married you for better or worse, and I'm going to put my trust in you." Nick replied.

"That's what you are supposed to do! I am your wife. And I want to hear no more shit about what somebody said about me on the streets. Because when the day comes that I think you don't trust me anymore, I will pack my shit and leave. They're plenty of guys waiting in line. Just don't fuck up! Understand!" Ny yelled back at Nick. She was full of anger when she realized that her husband had started accusing her.

"Yes, and here is the check; make sure you drop it off at the bank as soon as you get off. I want to make sure the check clears that I wrote for getting the car fix."

Nick said as he handed over the check to his wife.

"Okay then! I'm going to bed." Ny replied, took the check, and walked away.

Nick and Ny are fast asleep. Nick suddenly wakes up and looks at the clock.

It was 7:47 am. Nick realizes Ny is still in bed with him sleep. Nick wakes up Ny.

"Wake up! Wake up! You are going to be late for work?" Nick said as he tried to wake up his wife for work.

Ny wakes up and gets dressed. She then grabs her phone to call Leu Motors to let them know she is going to be late. She grabs Nick's check off of the dresser and heads out the door. Nick is yelling at Ny not to forget about dropping off the check at the bank. Ny does not respond. All Nick heard was the loud sound of the door closing. Nick then sits in the bed, puts his hands over his face, and starts shaking his head. Then he lays back down and goes to sleep.

ꙮ 4 Days Later: Outside Of Leu Motors

Nick is going in early to get some overtime. He comes across another employee names James, who works the day shift and he is leaving. They stop and talk to each other.

"What's happening, brother!" Nick asked James.

"Liking these days, man! You better come on in." James said with a smile.

"Naw! I'm a night man. I can't get up that early in the morning. That's why they call me Nick at night. HA! HA! Oh, by the way, have you seen my wife in here?" Nick answered. James is looking at Nick like he's crazy.

"Why in the hell are you looking at me like that for?" Nick asked as he couldn't understand why James was giving him that look.

"Nigeria Hines, they call her Ny. That is your wife, right!" James asked Nick.

Nick was shocked to know his wife's name from James. He then asks James, "You know that's my wife. What the fuck is going on?"

James gave a cold look to Nick and said, "Nick! They fired Ny over a month ago in a 5-day letter. You know how it is. Leu, send that letter out, and if you don't respond in 5 days, you are history. I heard the Union is trying to get her back. But you know, just like I do, when it comes to that 5-day letter, if the Union does get her back, it will be at least a year, if not longer, before they let her back in."

Hearing this, Nick almost dropped to his knees when he heard the news. James sees Nick's reaction and feels sorry for him.

"I'm sorry I had to be the one that told you," James said in an apologetic tone.

"I just can't believe this shit! James, I'm going to ask you something, and please tell me what you know. Has my wife been messing around with some of these guys in here?" Nick said he wasn't sure what was going on in his life. Too many questions clumped his mind.

"Do you really want me to answer that?" James asked Nick lifting his eyebrows. It sounded like he knew something Nick wasn't aware of.

"Yes, I do!" Nick replied sternly.

"I haven't seen it, but what I heard is that she has this bad gambling problem, and if you have enough money? You can get that pussy as long as you keep your mouth shut." James told him.

Nick had a flashback to when Ny said almost those very words to him when she was dealing with Don. Nick says goodbye to James and runs up to the personnel office to find out for himself if what James is saying is true. He asked the head of personnel if his wife had been fired, and they told him almost word for word what James had said. Nick walks out of the office as if somebody had just dropped the Nuclear Bomb on him. Nick had been working for about two hours, but he didn't have his mind on what he was doing. The supervisor comes walking over to Nick.

"Nick! This is the 4th time in 20 minutes you have missed something on your job. This isn't like you. What in the hell is going on?" The supervisor said in a stern tone.

Nick tells his supervisor everything he hears that day.

"It's a mother fucker to be the last one to know, and it's really hard when it's dealing with someone you love, like your wife. You are in no shape to work, Nick.

You have some family days coming, so I'm sending you home and get your head clear and come back Monday, and I will make sure you will get your overtime today." The supervisor said, rubbing his forehead out of stress.

Nick agrees with the supervisor and leaves. Nick has made it home and is walking thru the house yelling for Ny, but she is not there, nor is his son. Nick has a seat at the kitchen table, and some open letters catch his eye. One of the letters was a disconnection notice from the electric company, a disconnection notice from the gas company, and a disconnection notice from the phone company. Nick is going crazy. There is a knock on the door. Nick looks outside and sees the Police and some man in a suit. Nick opens the door.

"Can I help you?" Nick asked the man in the suit standing right before him.

"I am the Deputy Sheriff of St. Louis, Missouri, and your house has just been foreclosed on. Now get out!" The man shouted.

Nick couldn't believe what he heard. He was quite certain that there was some kind of mistake and said, "Wait a minute! There has got to be some kind of mistake!"

"This address is 125 Lindell." The deputy asked, looking closely at the papers in his hand.

"Yeah, for sure! That's right!" Nick replied. He was quite nervous about what the hell was going on.

"You are Nicolas Hines, and your wife is Nigeria Hines?" Deputy asked Nick.

"That's right!" Nick replied.

"Okay then! There is no mistake! Now get your ass out of here right now or go to jail." The deputy said, giving Nick a harsh look.

"Please give me a chance to get the money. I just found out today that my wife has a gambling habit and lost her job, and she has not been paying the bills." Nick begged the officer. He was certain that Ny had gambled all the money.

"Okay! I will make a deal with you. Your wife has screwed you around, and that has been happing a lot lately since they brought in these gambling boats. Your mortgage is $1,500.00 a month. You are three months behind, and that adds up to $4,500.00, now with late fees at $75.00 a month. That would be altogether $4,725.00. If you can come up with the money before we move all of your belonging out in this front yard, I will let you stay." The deputy tells Nick what he wants in detail.

Nick agrees and hops in his car, and drives to the bank. Nick goes to the bank to withdraw from the savings account, and the teller lets him know he has insufficient funds. Nick asks how much is in there, and the teller tells him ten bucks and nine cents. Nick is losing his mind.

"Well, maybe the money is in the checking account," Nick says. He couldn't understand what was going on. All of a sudden, he was surrounded by debts and other financial problems.

"This says a negative balance of $150.00," The teller said to Nick.

Nick pulled out his credit cards and asked for a cash advance of $4,725.00.

The teller shakes her head that the card is no good. Nick hands her another one, and that one is no good either.

"I know this one should work. It's a platinum card, and I have built up $20,000.00 worth of credit. I should be able to get at least $10,000.00 cash advance." Nick said, putting his premium platinum card on the counter.

"I am sorry, but all of your cards are max out, and looking at your record, they have been that way for the last three or four months, and it has been that long since they have received a payment. I'm sorry, Mr. Hines." The teller said. She was feeling bad for Nick now!

Nick walks out of the bank and gets into his car. He drives up to a place called Bud and Jerome's Moving and Storage, a good friend of his works. Nick walks in and asks for his friend Kevin. One of the employees went to go find him. Kevin comes from around the corner and gives Nick a hug. Nick explains what has happened to Kevin. Kevin and other employees of the moving company in a big truck follow Nick. Kevin parks the truck in Nick's driveway, and he and the other guys load it up as soon as the Deputy people bring it out. When everything was out of the house, the Deputy put a big lock on the door and stuck up a white sign that said FORECLOSURE. He tapped Nick on the shoulder and said," I'm sorry, son, but it happens to the best of us" Then he left. All of Ny's clothes are on the front lawn.

"Are you sure you don't want to take her clothes?" Kevin asked Nick.

"After what just happened, I'm completely done with that bitch! I am so mad! If I had a gun and saw her right now! I would blow her fucking head off and wouldn't think twice about it." Nick said. He was quite sure what to do with Ny now. He has had enough of her now.

"I know this is hard on you, man. To find out that your wife has lost her job, spent all of your money, and used up your resources and fucking men of the job to support her habit. You loved her so much that you trusted her with everything and gave her everything. The equity you took out of your house in New York cleared you $50,000.00, and you invested all of it into this house and now lost it all. So what, in the end, did she do for you? Lie! Did you know she was a liar when you met her?" Kevin said, putting his hand on his shoulder, trying to console him.

"Yes! But I never thought she would lie to me." Nick said. He was quite shocked at how Ny had been lying to him on his face.

"Listen to me, my brother! If a woman outright lies, you can never trust her again in life. The old saying goes just like this. If you lie, you will steal, and if you steal, you can get yourself or somebody else killed. If you think that's a lie? Think about what just happened. Ny lies, Ny steels, and you just said yourself, and if you had a gun, you would kill her." Kevin said.

"You're right! The only reason why I won't kill her is because my son needs a mother, but if it wasn't for that! She would be a dead bitch. I'm getting ready to go rent a hotel and go see a lawyer in the morning about a divorce. I will see you in two weeks to come and pay for my furniture. I love you, brother, and I don't know what I would have done without you." Nick said.

"That's what friends are for," Kevin answered with a smile.

Nick and Kevin say goodbye and then leave. It's 3:30 in the morning, and Ny is pulling up into the driveway. She gets out of the car, walks up to the front door, and sees that big padlock. She runs back to the car and grabs a flashlight, and runs back up to the front door, and she sees the sign that the Deputy left. Ny reads the sign FORECLOSURE, then flash the light inside the house and sees nothing in there. Ny flashes the light on the front lawn, and she sees all of her clothes. Ny read the sign again, broke down, and started crying.

XII

❧ 10 Years Later-Outside Ni's House

Ni's son Jr. is cutting the grass. Ny lives in a little starter home, far from the baby mansion she had with her ex-husband. Ny earned her degree in Business Administration while she was on welfare. For the last five years, she always changing jobs because she gets fired or because she can't get along with anybody, and a lot of that has to do with her messing around with the men she works with, and some of them are married to other women at the same workplace.

But Ny doesn't care. Especially if they offered her some money, she would have sex with them in a heartbeat. Ny is now 39 years old, and she still looks just as good and pretty as she did when she was 21. Ny has a little pouch, but her thighs, hips, butt, and breasts are so big, round, and shapely that it's not noticeable. And when the average man sees her, they want her and some of them at all costs. Ny is someone who could be considered a professional whore.

The last time she had just one man in her life was her ex-husband. Since then, she has always had 2 or 3 men. One of them would be the provider. A provider is a man who wants a woman at all costs and would give her anything he has to be with her. Money uses his car, house, and whatever it takes. These are the type of guys that are not used to being with a fine woman. Then Ny will have her lover.

The lover is someone who Ny really enjoys company. Goes out on dates with, loves their lifestyle, is attracted to him, loves going to bed with him, and if the lover doesn't have any money, then Ny will provide, but she will always make it up by getting it from the provider or some man that she occasionally have sex with when she needs some money. Ny has been known to go to sex parties, meet guys at their houses or hotel and have threesomes. Will occasionally do a strip party if the money is right. Ny will have sex anywhere and with anybody if the money is right. It's been a rumor that she has been with women from time to time, but no one really knows.

"Hurry up and cut that grass if you want me to take you to baseball practice," Ny said to her son.

"Okay! Jr said. Ny closes the door and the phone rings. Ny answers it, and it's her best friend, Paula.

"What's up, girl? Saturday night! What are we going to do?" Paula said as soon as Ny picked up the phone.

"My girl, Jasmin, from New York, is coming to town. She is going to stay with me for a few days, so you know we have to show her around." Ny replied. She was planning a night out with her girls.

"So, how is the job market?" Paula questioned Ny, knowing all about her job history, and screwed up the hire-and-fire game.

"Would you believe that I ran into a guy that I used to work on the line with at Leu Motors name Robert? Now he is in management and works in the personnel office. He told me that they have been looking for me for the last 8 or 9 years." Ny told her about how she ran into Robert, who used to be her co-worker.

"Are you serious?" Paula asked with her eye widened.

"Yes! He said a year after I had been fired that the Union had gotten my job back but couldn't nobody find me. He said that they asked Nick where I was, and he told them not to mention that bitch name to me anymore. But, anyway, Robert told me to come back in and fill out an application because I'm officially terminated.

When you have been gone longer than you were there, then you're out of the Union, and the process has to start all over again. Going to orientation, taking tests, police reports, and whatever else." Ny said.

"Now that you have your degree. They may hire you in as supervisor." Paula reminded Ny how her life could be better than she had lived before.

"And that would just fuck Nick's ass up. Not only to see me back in there but now I'm your boss too. HA! HA!" Ny said with an egoistic laugh.

"When do you go in?" Paula replied, ignoring the boss part Ny had just said.

"He told me Tuesday morning at 9:00 am," Ny replied.

"Good luck, girl, and I will be there to pick up you and your girl from New York at about 8:30 pm. Goodbye!" Paula said and hung up the phone.

Inside A Night Club Called Hadleys Ny, Paula, and Jasmin are sitting at the table with drinks in front of them. The place is packed, and Ny's table is drawing a lot of attention from the guys that are in there. Ny's man is the owner of the club. He is an okay guy until he sees someone trying to hit on Ny. He gets jealous and comes from behind the bar and acts a fool with whoever's flirting with her. Ny loves that kind of attention. Sometimes she winks at guys just to get their attention so she can see her man act a fool over her.

"Where is that crazy ass man of yours? We ain't supposed to be buying no drinks in here." Paula looked at Ny and said. All three of them shared the same traits of hanging around with the boys.

"Who is your man?" Jasmin asked Ny.

"The owner of the club," Paula replied.

"You got it like that, Ny? Jasmin asked Ny. She wanted to know how every time she got hitched up with shit-rich men.

"He is one of the few guys that provide, that I am attracted to, but he doesn't have any social skills. He acts up every time we go somewhere, and if a man looks at me or talks to me, he will act a fool." Ny replied.

She was quite proud of her charm and ability to control men with just a smile and flirty eyes.

"Everybody has their faults," Jasmin said with a wide smile covering her face.

"Speak of the devil. Here he comes now." Jasmin as she saw a handsome Man approaching their table. It was the owner of the club. He comes over to Ny and gives her a kiss.

"This is my girl Jasmin from New York, and this is my man, Motubu," Ny said, introducing Jasmin and Motubu to each other.

"Nice to meet you. Are you from Africa?" Jasmin asked him as they shook hands.

"Yes! And it is a pleasure to meet you. Drinks on the house." Motubu replied, with one hand tucked in his pocket and the other wrapped around Ny's waist.

"It's about time. I can't keep on buying this high ass shit." Paula said.

Walking in comes a well dress handsome man. He is a little drunk, and he is shaking hands and hugging a lot of people in the club. This guy catches Jasmin's attention.

"That must be the St. Louis Player right there," Jasmin said, pointing out to a Man.

"How do you know? Because I do see him with a lot of women." Paula asked Jasmin.

"Look at how he is caring for himself. He hasn't been in here for 5 minutes, and he is holding one girl's hand while he is trying to get the attention of another woman. From the way he was acting and looking, I think he got his drink on a little early." Jasmin replied, making Paula and Ny realize all the minor actions he was doing and what these actions actually meant.

"Your right! That dude tries to hit on me all the time, but he's always so drunk says Ny and he never remembers who I am. He always has the same line. I am The-Lou in The Lou."

"And that's something your ego can't take," Paula replied to Ny.

"Not when it's coming from a drunk. Don't play! And here he comes." Ny replied in a bit serious tone. Just as Jasmin, Ny, and Paula are talking, the man starts walking toward Ny's table until he stops by a man he knows that works there. They hug and shake hands.

"What's up, The-Lou? Looking good, brother. You know you be wearing those suits." The worker said, praising his style.

"Thanks, brother. I got to do something to try and get some of these women out here that can bring something to the table other than their legs wide open. You know this is my first time in here." The-Lou replied.

"In that case, your first drink is on me. Let me get my ass back behind this bar and go to work. Just come up when you're ready. In a minute, brother." The worker humbly said. The-Lou then starts walking over to Ny's table and introduce himself, and shakes their hands.

"Where I am from, men don't shake a lady's hand when he meets her," Jasmin said.

"Okay! Well, how about I stick my tongue down your throat." The-Lou replied in A joking way.

"What did you say?" Jasmin said angrily. She was quite pissed off by his response.

"I'm just playing, but as fine as you are. I wouldn't mind." The-Lou smiled and said. "So, where are you from?" He continued showing some interest in Jasmin.

"New York City," Jasmin replied rudely.

"I have some friends in the N.Y.C., the Bronx, and every last one of them mother fucker's talks just like Mike Tyson. As a matter of fact, you talk just like Mike Tyson too. HA! HA!" The-Lou said, giving a sarcastic laugh.

"Hey, baby! When are me and you going to hang out?" The-Lou said, looking at Ny.

"How come you don't ever remember me?" Ny asked him, as he always flirts with her whenever he see's her.

"Did you ever give me your phone number? Or did you ever take mines?" The-Lou asked Ny.

"I never gave you my number, but I did take yours a couple of times," Ny replied.

"Well, what in the hell do you expect? I'm not going to be remembering anybody that acts like they don't want to be bothered. Too many women out here for that." The-Lou replies carelessly. He wouldn't give a damn for a woman who doesn't pay attention to him.

Motubu is looking at The-Lou talking to Ny, and he is getting jealous and comes from around the bar and approaches The-Lou, the worker behind the bar follows in behind Motubu.

"Hey! Stop talking to my woman!" Mobutu said angrily. He couldn't stand The-Lou anymore talking to Ny.

"How am I supposed to know this is your woman? I don't see no damn sign on her back." The-Lou replied.

"Hey! This is a misunderstanding. Motubu, this is a brother I go back with. He's cool; now come on, and let's get back behind the bar." One of the workers came forward and tried to cool down the guys before their anger could turn violent.

Motubu gives The-Lou an angry look and leaves. The-Lou is watching him all the way.

"Now I understand why you don't give your phone number out. Let me get my ass out of here before someone gets hurt." The-Lou was sensible enough to leave. The Worker talks to Motubu.

"Motubu, you have to stop running your customers away because some of them are talking to Ny. She knows how you are, and still, she comes in here and talks and flirts with these men just to watch you get all pissed off. Now that dude The-Lou just left, he is a nice guy, but he has a brother, and everybody calls him Will-Die. And the reason they call him Will-Die is that you start some shit with him, either you will die, or he will die, and the last time I check, he is still living, but a whole lot of other mother fuckers ain't." The worker said, trying to convince Mobutu to control his anger before he losses too much.

"And Will-Die ain't the only guy in St. Louis that thinks that way. I know you are from Africa, and you all are very possessive over your women, but this is the United States, and if you piss off some of these brothers here. They will walk up into this club and open fire, and I don't want to be here if that happens, so please chill!" The worker continues.

Motubu nods his head, then he looks at the dance floor and sees Ny dancing with some man, and he starts to get mad all over again. The worker calls his name, then looks at him. Motubu holds his hands up like he is okay.

It's Tuesday, and Ny is sitting in the personnel office at Leu Motors. Robert comes from the back of the office where the Head Plant Manager is. He walks up to Ny.

"Are you sure you want to go for a supervisor position?" Robert asked Ny. He wanted to ensure that Ny knew what she was asking for.

"Any doubt?" Ny said and paused for a while. "Let me put it that way, I have my degree, and I'm going to put it to use," Ny said, telling Robert that she is qualified for the post.

Just as they were having the discussion, the Plant Manager entered.

"Sir! Your interview is here. Ms. Nigeria Hines." Robert introduces Ny to the Plant Manager; with this, he picks up the papers and leaves the room.

"Well, hello, pretty lady! How are you doing today?" Plant Manager said with a welcoming smile.

"Just fine and yourself" Ny answered.

"Before we get this interview started. The one thing I would like to know is, do you still have that fat, sweet, good pussy." The Plant Manager asked with a wierd look and cliché smile.

Ny was shocked by his claim. She almost fell out of her seat when she heard that.

"What! I mean, are you serious." Ny asked in disbelief. She wasn't sure what was happening and how on Earth why the plant manager said that to her.

"I see that you do not recognize me. Since the last time you saw me, I have put on about 50 pounds. I'm bald with grey sides and wearing glasses. How long has it been? I would say about 15 years. Yes, I am serious. Serious enough to divorce my wife because you said you loved me and wanted to marry me." Said the Plant Manager. He was Don, the sugar daddy Ny had 15 years back.

"DON GREYBOOK?" Ny exclaimed. She now very well knew who she was talking to.

"That's right! When I got wind that you took the transfer to St. Louis, I called down here, but didn't nobody know who you were. I remember your last name, but I couldn't remember your first. I was just so used to calling you Ny. I asked them to look up anyone with the last name of Baker, and the only thing they came up with was John Baker. So yes! I felt like a fool, being used, and the worst part about it. I left a good woman and lost a lot of money behind it for a woman I never was going to have because she married somebody else before she left New York and came to St. Louis. That's why they had no record of you because your name had changed. I just want you to know that you destroyed me with your lies." Don said, telling her all about what he had faced because of her.

"I'm so sorry!" Ny said, trying to sound guilty.

"I was going to come down here and look for you myself, but those two detectives came by my house and told me that I couldn't leave the state because they think that I broke into my own apartment and I'm being investigated for insurance fraud. Did I ask them? How do you know that Ny didn't set this up? Now this is in their own words. I will never forget what they said."

Why would a pretty young girl want to take a chance on going to jail over an old fat fucker like you when she already has a young stud who might have just as much money as you? After you bought her the car, the writing was on the wall, and all good things come to an end, but you didn't want it to end. So you had her broken in on and let your boys rape her. But the key is, why would she take the damn toilet ? What in the hell is she going to do with that?

You can put it in another one of your apartments and have the insurance by you another one. They wouldn't let me leave the state for a year and a half. They ended up dropping the case because of a lack of evidence. But if DNA was as popular back then as it is now. I would bet anything that was Mr. Hines's semen on you." Don said.

"I am sorry. I was young and stupid; please forgive me." She replied, trying not to sound foolish at that time.

"That was a long time ago, and so much has happened. I need three supervisors. I'm going to make my decision on Friday, but if you're really sorry! Come spend the night with me for the next three nights. Oh, by the way, did I tell you that the job starts at $80,000.00 a year plus a bonus of anywhere from ten to twenty thousand a year? Here is my cell number; call me, and I will tell you what Hotel to meet me at." Don said, handing his business card to her.

Ny takes Don up on his offer. She spends the next three nights with Don being his sex slave. It's Friday morning, and Don and Ny are getting dressed.

"Well! You got the job! Report Monday morning at 7:00 am. Oh, by the way. I always wanted to know is, why you took the toilet."

"I was just as shocked as you were that it was gone. Come to find out, one of my cousins needed it, so my other cousin, that is a carpenter, and Plummer took it for him. I didn't know they cost that much until I had to replace a toilet in my home." Ny replied she wasn't prepared a bit to confront all of her lies out of the blues, but still, she was content.

"Like I said, see you Monday. Welcome back!" Don said.

Ny is so happy! She is on cloud nine! She thanks Don and runs out the door.

She gets on her cell phone calling everybody she knows, including her parents in New York, to tell them the good news. Ny is trying to call Paula, but she is not answering her phone. Ny drives over to Paula's house, and she sees her planting some flowers. Ny jumps out of her car, yelling, "I got the job"! A big smile comes over Paula's face as they hug each other.

"Well, this calls for a celebration!" Paula said she wanted to celebrate Ny's victory of getting a well-paid job.

Ny runs down the whole story to Paula about Don, going all the way back from the start of how she met in New York to how it ended up this morning in the hotel.

"Girl, you know you are a hoe, but you used that body to get what you want.

Now that you're getting a second chance, don't mess up, and please don't start gambling again." Paula said and requested Ny not to get into something that leaves her dipped in debt once again.

"That's something you will never have to worry about. I still see that big FORECLOSURE sign in my mind right now, and it cost me one man to this day I truly loved. He will never forgive me. But it's going to fuck his ass up when I walk back up in there, and I am his boss. HA! HA!" Ny replies and starts giggling.

Ny thought that she had successfully landed a job as a supervisor at Lue Motors, and despite Don's initial hesitation, he eventually agreed to give her the position. With a salary of $80,000 per year, Ny felt like she had won the ultimate victory. However, Ny couldn't help but feel a sense of guilt for her selfish actions. She knew that she had caused a great deal of trouble for Don and his family, and she couldn't shake the feeling that karma would eventually catch up with her.

Nonetheless, she pushed those thoughts to the back of her mind and focused on her new job, determined to succeed and make a better life for herself.

XIII

*N*y is waiting in line behind two other people. A woman comes from around the corner and asks all of them if they are the new supervisors that were hired by Mr. Greybrook. They all said yes. The woman handed them some papers and asked them to fill them out. The woman collects the papers and then starts calling out their names.

"June Jones" The woman calls out the name.

The woman named June Jones raised her hand and said out loud, "Here!"

"Nancy Smith?" The woman called out the name of the second lady.

"Here!" The lady named Nancy Smith raised her hand and said.

"Sherri May" The woman called the name of the third woman.

"No! My name is Nigeria Hines." Ny said as she was expecting her name to be called out.

The woman started looking thru her papers and said," I don't see Nigeria Hines" Right then, a woman came walking thru the door, and she said," I am Sherri May, and I was told by Don Greybrook to be here at 7:00 am. I hope I'm in the right place."

"Yes, you are. I want you three to follow me and Mrs. Hines. Please stay here until I get back, and we are going to find out what went wrong." The woman said and took all the ladies with her.

"Where is he?" Ny asked. She was quite taken aback, and all her senses were blacked out. She had no idea what was going on!

"Friday was his last day. He retired and went back to New York." The woman told her and went back to her office. After a while, she came back with a letter in her hand.

"Here, I found this letter he left for you. We will be hiring so more supervisors next week, so I would guess that is what that letter is about, telling you when to come back in. I gotta go; hope to see you soon, Mrs. Hines." The woman said, handing the piece of paper to her.

Ny opens up the letter! The letter read "HELLO! NY, AND IF YOU ARE READING THIS. YOU JUST GOT FUCKED AND YOUR NOT GETTING THE JOB! YOU KNOW THAT PAYBACK IS A MOTHER FUCKER. GOODBYE BITCH!!!!! HA! HA! HA!"

Ny drops the letter and slowly walks out the door. She is in a state of shock.

NY gets into her car and starts thinking about everybody she told she had the job.

NY pulls over on the side of the street and starts crying like a baby.

❧ Inside The-Lou's House

The Lou is in bed and with 2 naked women one on each side of him. The Lou wakes up walks into a back bedroom and looks out the window at his inground pool and the water looks great. He walks back into his bed room and wake up the women and tell them they have to leave. The women get dress and one of them say, "had a great time Luther baby, when can we do this again?" The-Lou says soon. both of the women give The-Lou a kiss then they leave. The Lou pulls out of his 2 car Garage driving his Drop Top Red Jaguar. He listening to Bitch Better Have My Money and singing along with it. His phone rings and it's Vicky. The-Lou says Hello, Vicky says Luther are we going to the Movies today? The-Lou answers yes "if I can hold on to those big ass titties while your making love to me". Vicky says is that all you want from me is some Pussy? The-Lou says (in a intellectual voice) Well that's just simply not true. (back to his regular voice and he raising it) I want some money too but your broke ass ain't got none of that, so I can only get the only thing you have to offer and that's Pussy! Vicky says you see, that's what's wrong with you and some of these guys, y'all don't know how to be men anymore. The-Lou says, I will call you back later, I got to take this call. It's Mary on the other end. So are you still coming over here says Mary? The-Lou says I don't know, you be acting like you don't want to have sex. Mary says why should I? Why buy the Cow when you can get the Milk for free, The-Lou says Look here! I am the Mother Fuckin Farmer and I have plenty of Cows so what in the Fuck do I look like buying some damn Milk!" Mary says you see!! that's is what's wrong with your Punk Ass! Cheap Mother Fucker, Don't call me no more!! The-Lou says you the one that just called me! Mary hangs up the phone angerly. The-Lou is still Driving and the phone rings and its Sandy and she says if your not busy today Luther, can I bring my kids over to swim? The-Lou says, you brought them last time you came, I want to spend some alone time with you. you always want to bring your kids, this ain't Daddy Day Care over here! Sandy' Well if my kids can't come, Fuck You and your Swimming Pool too! The phone rings again, this time it's Nicky. Hello Luther, are we still on for this afternoon? Yes says The-Lou. Nicky says will 2 o clock be good? Yes says The Lou. Nicky "see you then goodbye" The-Lou is pulling up to the store and parks his car and starts walking.

❧ Outside Of A Grocery Store

Paula is parked on the side, waiting on someone to come out. She sees The-Lou walking up into the store. Paula calls him. The-Lou walks up to her car.

"How are you doing? Don't you remember me and my friend Ny?" Paula said she moved forward to greet him.

"Where is Ty? He was supposed to call me." The-Lou asked Paula.

"I didn't say Ty. I said Ny. And Ny is a female. And you always try to talk to her every time you see her. Is that your Convertible Jaguar, I saw you pull up in?"

"That's my car, but who is this Ny person? Can you call her?" The-Lou replied.

Paula calls Ny on her cell phone and hands it to The-Lou. They talk for a minute.

The-Lou gives Ny his phone number and hands Paula back her phone.

"Do you remember her now?" Paula asked him, showing him Ny's picture on her phone.

The-Lou shakes his head no. Paula gives The-Lou an invitations to her party and tells him Ny will be there. The-Lou said "Ok I will be there"

The Lou has made it back home and Nicky comes walking thru the door, Nicky is not the prettiest woman in the World but she has a great body and that always make up for a woman not having a pretty face. Nicky says hello Luther, I have been waiting to see you. here is the 5th of Hennessy you asked for, I put the Beer in the fridge and your smokes are on the kitchen table, plus I got us some Stake dinners from outback. The-Lou thanks her. Nicky says to The-Lou, I have been wanting to talk to you about something and its been on my mind heavy. The-Lou "Ok spit it out" Nicky says" We have been spending some time together, but I want to see you more and I think that me and you should have a monogamy relationship. The-Lou look at her and said "I got to much going on for that type of relationship. I got too many bills, child support then The-Lou pulls out his mortgage statement book and slams that down on the table and says to her you see how much I pay a month? It's $1,050.00 are you ready to deal with this? Nicky look at the statement then looked at The-Lou and said she would be right back. 30 minutes later, Nicky comes thru the door and slams 6,300.00 down on the table and says this is for the 1st 6 months and its a lot more where that came from, all you have to do is let me and my daughter move in with you. The-Lou was caught off guard, because when women would talk to him about being one on one or moving in, throwing down the mortgage payment book would scare them off. This is a great offer, The-Lou like Nicky but not that much that he could look at her everyday. The-Lou said "Damn baby! I really would like to take you up on this, but you know I see other Women and the truth be told, I am not ready to just settle down with just one woman. Nicky says well that is one thing I do love about you is that you are honest. The-Lou thanks her and they ate, drank and had sex and then Nicky left. About an hour later it's about 5pm, The-Lou other lady comes over name Joyce, The-Lou has been knowing her since he was 18 years old, she was not his type at all, but she was always so good to him, he just couldn't let her go. Joyce came in and handed The-Lou an envelope and it was 2,500.00 dollars in it. Joyce says my settlement came in from when I fell at The Department Store and this is for you Baby! The-Lou thanks her then Joyce says pull down those pants so I can suck that Dick! That's another thing that kept her around, no woman The-Lou has ever been with could give a blow Job like Joyce, plus she knew what kind of man The-Lou was and never question him about anything, she was just glad when it was her turn to see him.later on that evening, The-Lou walked into St. Louis Nites, he was at the Bar ordering a drink when a very sexy woman came up to him and introduce herself as Jasmin from Chicago, She said "I have been seeing you around driving that drop Top Jag, so I ask some of my people about you and they all vouch for you saying you are about your business, You have I think a 4 Bedroom house with a swimming pool and I heard your swim parties are nothing short of what some Hollywood celebrities would be having. The-Lou said "well the guys that set it up told me that they was going to make me look like Neno Brown from New Jack City" and they both started laughing! Jasmin said" I am going to get right down to the point, I have 4 girls with me and we are looking for a place to stay in St. louis, now if you let me and my 4 Girls come live with you, if your house cost 200,000.00 we could have it paid off in 3 months plus you get the benefits of having all 5 of us whenever you got ready, we just need to use your house to make our money. The-Lou says that is a great offer, but how come you just don't go and rent a house? Why me? Jasmin says I don't want my name tide to nothing and what I am doing is illegal, You are a single man and you have a lot of traffic, so it won't be that noticeable and by it being the beginning of summer, we could have sex pool parties almost everyday and watch that money start pouring in. The-Lou almost couldn't believe what he was hearing. The-Lou said "Let me have your number, I want to think about this. Jasmin gave The-Lou her number. The next day The-Lou called Jasmin and he said to her, I want to thank you for this opportunity but I am not going to do this, the reason is that when your doing things illegal I could lose everything trying to get rich quick. Yes I do have a lot of traffic but 5 women having men coming over and having parties everyday would get notice. Jasmin said "by the the time the Summer ends, we could have made a lot of money and I don't think your neighbors or The Law can tell you what to do in your own house! The-Lou said "If you know anything about the trickery of The Law, they will come up with Laws you never heard of and get false witnesses and these things happen all the time and that's a chance I am not willing to take. Thanks, but no thanks. Jasmin said she understood and hung up the phone. The real reason The-Lou didn't do it is because when you make illegal money and it's going to be a lot of it, there is going to be a very good chance your going have to get Blood on your hands, for instance, if one of these customers get angry and violent, The-Lou is going to have to do something about it, beat the dude up or maybe have to kill him and in his mind, the risk is not worth the reward!

Later that night, The-Lou went to Paula's party, and she showed him who Ny was.

The-Lou went over to talk to Ny, but she acted like she didn't want to be bothered, and The-Lou wasn't overly impressed himself. The-Lou got his drink on, then left. Almost a year later,

The-Lou is leaving a nightclub called St. Louis Nites, and he sees Paula standing at the door. He speaks to Paula, and she points at Ny. He went over to talk to Ny, and this time, she gave The-Lou her phone number. The-Lou and Ni's first date was a concert; He wasn't sure if Ny was going to show, so he also invited Mary and it was about 8 other people that met up over The-Lou house for a few drinks before the concert and then Ny came walking in. The-Lou intoduce Ny to everyone including Mary. The-Lou cousin Sandra said to everyone when Mary step out for a minute and Ni was in the Restroom, I can't believe this shit! I never seen A man Have

2 dates at the same time, then they all started laughing. After the concert, everyone went to St. Louis Nites except Mary who The-Lou rode to the concert with. Mary went home so The-Lou rode to the club with Ny. The-Lou knows the bouncer at the club, and they even went out and had a few drinks together. Ny was dating the bouncer at the nightclub they were at but did not tell The-Lou. When Ny and The-Lou walked into the Club, they were with a lot of people in The-Lou's crew, so the bouncer didn't think twice about Ny being with The-Lou until he saw them get into her car together and pull off.

❧ Outside Of The-Lou's House

Ny and The-Lou had just finished their dinner and drinks and were now sitting in the car, feeling a bit tipsy. Ny couldn't help but feel grateful that The-Lou had given her a chance, despite not liking him much initially. She looked over at him and smiled, feeling content and happy.

"You know, I still can't believe how far we've come," she said, her voice soft.

"When we first met, you didn't seem to like me very much." The-Lou chuckled, shaking his head.

"Yeah, I'll admit, I didn't really think much of you at first. But you've proven me wrong, You're not the same person you were back then." Ny smiled, feeling a sense of pride in herself.

"I really had fun, Luther. You're not the arrogant drunk I thought you were. Now that I think about it, you're a really nice guy." Ny said.

"Thank you. And you're not the stuck-up ass woman I thought you were. So when am I going to see you again?" The-Lou replied.

"Well, I do have a guy, but he hasn't been acting right lately. But long as you understand that, we can see each other, and please! Keep your mouth shut." Ny told her and giggled playfully.

"Everybody has somebody," The-Lou said, shrugging his shoulder.

"And we know you have somebody. I have seen you out with all of those different women. I remember you, but you don't remember me. I have been seeing you for the last 4 or 5 years, and every time you see me, you try to hit on me." Ny said, giving him a sarcastic look.

"Now that you have kicked it with me, I will remember you from now on. If you're not doing anything Friday, come over and let me cook your dinner for you. I used to be a chef before I started working for the Ford Motor Company." The-Lou said and winked at her.

"I just might take you up on that," Ny said and laughed.

❦ Inside The-Lou's House-Friday Night

Ny and The-Lou are drinking cognac, and Ny is starting to get loose. Ny takes off her shirt and gets up, and starts dancing. Ny has on a low-cut bra and jeans that show every curve she has. The-Lou can't take his eyes off Ny. He had no idea that she had a body like that. Ny looks just as good or, if not better, than any woman he has seen on T.V. or in a magazine. The way she was dancing and moving around, he had never seen professional stripers move and dance like that. The-Lou is really turned on now. Ny motions him to get up and come dance with her. Ny starts feeling The-Lou and pressing her body against his. The-Lou starts doing the same thing to her. Ny is down to nothing, but her panty, and The-Lou has her bra in his hand. The-Lou takes off his pants, and then Ny stops him.

"Remember, I did tell you I had a guy," Ny said. She wanted to see if he would get angry or not.

The-Lou looked at Ny and said," Okay" Then he went and sat down on the sofa and fixed himself another drink and asked her if she was ready for another one. Ny couldn't believe that he didn't get mad, offer her some money, or start begging like most of the men that she comes in contact with.

The-Lou was so smooth to the point that he was the first man she had been with that reminded her of her ex-husband. She is attracted to him, he got his shit together, and he is not tripping off of her or whatever she does. This impressed Ny.

"A lot of guys would have gotten mad and said I was teasing them, but you didn't," Ny said, looking at The-Lou.

"Get mad for what? Pussy is one of the easiest things to get. It's finding a woman I really like that has her shit together is what's hard." The-Lou replied, showing that he wasn't concerned a bit about Ny having another guy.

"Yea! But you aren't ever had none this pussy here, and I got my shit together.

I have my own house, car, and degree. Don't play!" Ny said she was now getting pissed.

"Let me tell you this, fat round ass, flat ass, once a man busts a nut, it all feels the same," The-Lou replied to Ny.

"Okay, dude! We will see about that." Ny snatches her bra out of The-Lou's hand and started putting back on her clothes and to her surprise The-Lou didn't try to stop her and she couldn't believe it. All of a sudden, this is becoming a small challenge for Ny.

The-Lou asked Ny if she would like to go have a drink with him at Mrs. Wicks this Sunday Ny acted like she may have something to do, but in reality, she couldn't wait for Sunday to get here.

❧   Outside Of Mrs. Wicks

Mrs. Wicks just closed. Ny and The-Lou are talking to The-Lou's friends Bobby, KDog, and Lil Joe. Everybody agrees that they want to go somewhere else. The-Lou suggested that they go to St. Louis Nites. Everybody was in agreement, but when Ny heard that, she thought about the bouncer and changed her mind.

"Luther, I really don't want to go there; I'm kind of tired. How about we go back to your house and listen to some music and spend the rest of the night with each other." Ny said to The-Lou. She was hell-tired and wanted to rest.

❧   Inside The-Lou's House

The-Lou is making Ny a drink. While Ny is busy looking at The-Lou and thinking that he has some charm that the other guys never had.

"The-Lou, I have seen all of your house except upstairs. Show it to me," Ny said.

She wanted to make a move.

The-Lou takes Ny upstairs and shows her the bedrooms. When The-Lou shows Ny his bedroom, she jumps right in the bed. She starts moving around like she is trying to get comfortable.

"I am more tired than I thought; you don't mind if I lay here for a minute, do you?" Ny asked The-Lou, but definitely, her intention wasn't to rest at all.

Ny is lying on her back as she slides down in the bed, and her dress is rising up. Ny opens her legs as wide as she can. The-Lou jumped on top of her, and they started kissing. Then he takes Ni's dress off and starts making love to her. No woman ever made him feel like this in the bedroom, but he didn't let Ny know that. When they were finished making love, The-Lou turned over and went to sleep. Ny just knew that he was going to act like the rest of the men, but he didn't, and this reminded Ny more of her ex-Nick.

Ny was starting to fall for him a little. Her intention was to see if she could get any money out of him, but now she realizes that she actually likes him. 2 weeks have passed, and Ny and The-Lou are with each other every day. 2 months passed, and The-Lou is spending six nights out of 7 over Ny's house. She is the only woman that he sees;

The-Lou very rarely go out with his friends, and when he does, Ny is right there with them.

Ny is impressed with how popular he is. Where ever they go to a club, concert, or out to dinner. People are always coming up to him and shaking his hand.

This is the happiest The-Lou had ever been in his life, to the point that he is not hiding his emotions anymore. They would be lying in bed, and Ny would always say, this is like a marriage, and he agreed because up until now, the marriage had never crossed his mind.

❧ Inside Ny's House

Ny is going through something in her room, and The-Lou is sitting on the bed watching T.V. Ny shows him a man's gold Rolex watch.

"Is that for me?" The-Lou asked. He was surprised to see the watch.

"No! It belongs to that crazy African I used to date." Ny. said.

"Why don't you give it back to him?" The-Lou questioned Ny.

"Because if I do that, he will start calling me again. Sometimes he just disappears, and I won't see him for months. Besides, I have a restraining order on him. He can't come around me." Ny said she was not interested in hitching up with him.

"You need to give that man back his watch if you don't have anything else to do with him," The-Lou said in a quite serious tone.

"Don't worry! I got this, dude." Ny replied, making him feel confident that she would return the watch to Motubu.

2 Months Later-Outside The-Lou's House-Backyard

The-Lou has a lot of his relatives over at his house from in and out of town. They're here for a family reunion, including his brother Will-Die who now lives in Kansas City.

The-Lou relatives are everywhere, some of them are swimming in the pool, and some of them are in the house playing pool or sitting around drinking and watching live concerts on DVD.

"Luther, what spot are we going to hit tonight?" Will-Die asked The-Lou.

"We are going to go to Two Brothers, then to Hadleys. Our cousin, Johnnie from Houston, is here, and he wants to go out too." The-Lou replied.

"Is that all who is going?" Will-Die asked

"No! We are going to ride with my woman Ny, and her friend Paula is supposed to be coming too."

"You think I can get with her?" Will-Die said. He wanted to spend a night in bed with her.

"No! She is married, but my boy Pep is coming, and he is going to have his lady Fran with him. When I talk to him, I will ask him if Fran has any friends." The-Lou said, getting Will-Die's attention off Ny and diverting him to some other topic.

"This woman done got to your ass! I remember the days when I would come to town, and you would have shit set up, now that you did fall in love. You got to go ask your partner's women. Do they have anybody I can meet?" Will-Die said as he saw the spark of love in The-Lou's eyes for the very first time.

❧ Inside two Brothers

The-Lou, Ny, Will-Die, Johnnie, and Paula are sitting at a table finishing up their drinks.

"I am ready to go!" The-Lou said.

"Hold on a minute. I want to see what this little dame looks like your boy Pep and his gal supposed to be bringing up here." Will-Die said.

The-Lou agrees to wait. Pep and Fran come walking in with Pep's friend Rodger.

"Well, that's who they brought up here for you to meet; now, are you ready to go," The-Lou said.

"What's up, Luther, Will-Die, Ny, and everybody else? This is my lady Fran and my boy Rodger." Pep asked everyone.

"Man, what took you so long? We are getting ready to leave and go to Hadleys. I have my cousin Johnnie here from Houston, and I want to show him around before it gets too late." The-Lou said, looking at his watch.

"Well, go on ahead and go. And we'll meet you all up there." Pep said.

❧ Inside Hadleys

Ny and Paula walk right in and find a seat in the back of the club. The-Lou stopped to talk to some people he knew. The-Lou, Will-Die, and Johnnie found Ny and Paula and had a seat next to them. Ny is laughing hard, and so is Paula. The-Lou is just looking at them.

"Someone is hating on you, dude! HA! HA!" Ny said, trying hard to control her laughter.

"What in the hell are you talking about?" The-Lou asked in a pissed-off manner.

"That guy Motubu she used to go with is in here," Paula said, controlling her laughter.

"The one whose gold Rolex you have?" The-Lou asked, turning to Ny.

"Yes! And he is hating on you, dude. HA! HA!" Ny said and rolled out in laughter. A few minutes later, Motubu comes to where they all are. He said excuse me to The-Lou and he moved and let him talk to Ny.

"When can I come and get my watch? I tried calling you, but you won't answer. When can I come and get my watch?" Mobutu asked Ny. He wanted to get his watch as soon as possible.

"You can't. I will get it to you." Ny said sternly.

Motubu leaves, and a few minutes later, Pep, Fran, and Rodger walk in. Pep was looking at The-Lou and asked him what was wrong.

"Her ex-man is here, and there might be a problem," The-Lou said, pointing to Ny and telling them what just happened.

As soon as The-Lou said that, Motubu came back over asking for his watch. Now Motubu is starting to get on everybody's nerves. Fran walked over to where Ny was and got between her and Motub; then, everybody stood up. Motubu sees this, then walks off. The-Lou is mad.

"I told you a long time ago to give that man back what belongs to him,". He was quite angry about why Ny didn't listen to him in the first place.

"Well, you know he disrespected you," Paula told him.

"No, he didn't! The 1st thing is that you and Ny walk in by yourselves. He did see me come in with you two. The 2nd thing is that when he did come over, he said excuse me, he wasn't trying to punk anybody. The 3rd thing is that I can't blame him for asking for his watch. And Ny is sitting up here acting like she doesn't want to give it to him. Ny told me she had a restraining order against him. So he can't just show up at her house. He said he tried to call, but she won't answer. So now that he sees her, here is his opportunity to talk to her about what's his." The-Lou said he wasn't able to control his anger.

"We will come back up here next Friday, and I will give him his watch then because this is his hang-out every Friday," Ny said.

"What! You knew he was going to be here, and you let us come anyway, knowing you have his watch and he was going to ask for it. What in the hell are you trying to do? Get some shit started? Now that I think about it, I remember you telling me that other guys that you met were going to get with him because he hit you." The-Lou said. He was quite outrageous and wanted to know the reason why Ny didn't listen to him.

"Well, I'm glad you were not drinking and didn't say anything because it probably would have been some trouble," Ny replied, trying to keep calm.

"The only reason I didn't say anything the 2nd time he came over was because, on Fridays, when you are caught fighting, they will lock you up for the whole weekend. I have a lot of my family from out of town staying with me, and the only one who knows his way around is my brother, who is leaving tomorrow morning.

And I couldn't take that chance on going to jail, and the more I think about it, all this bullshit could have been avoided if you would have done as I said and given him back his watch." The-Lou said.

"Fuck that Nigga! Where does he live, Ny? I will walk up to his door and hand him the mother fucker. Just fuck that Nigga. I am from the 3rd Ward in Houston, and we will do any and every. It doesn't matter, so just fuck that nigga! I got your back, Cousin Johnnie said.cousin if he would have made a move? I am telling you right now! That would have been the last one he would have made." Johnnie said he, too, was mad by now.

"You see what I mean, NY? Now he is ready to hurt somebody over something you could have avoided. And I didn't bring him out here for this." The night was now all ruined.

"Luther is right, Ny, and I do not agree with him because he is my brother, but you don't want to take a chance on getting somebody hurt over some shit like this. Just give that man back his watch and be done with it." Will-Die said, agreeing with The-Lou.

"Will-Die, you will bust a cap in a mother fucker faster than I will; I can't believe you are talking like that?" Johnnie asked Will-Die.

"Johnnie, you don't go around hurting nobody over shit like this," Will-Die warned Johnnie. He didn't want to land in trouble.

"Well, I'm thinking about what you said. Now that I thought about it. Fuck that nigga!" Johnnie said.

They all leave the club, and Ny drops off The-Lou and his family. Will-Die and Johnnie go inside the house. The-Lou stays in the car and talks to Ny.

"I love you, Ny, but don't knowingly put me or my family in a situation like this again! Give that man back his watch, and let that be the end of it. But let's get all of this shit out the way. I used to wonder why you never wanted to go to St. Louis Nites, and I have a V.I.P. Card there, and when you finally told me, it's because you were fucking one of the guys that work there. But you never told me who it was. Now I want to know who he is, and I want to know right now!" The-Lou said. He didn't want to get any more trouble over Ny.

"Okay! I will tell you. It was David." Ny answered.

"The bouncer, David," The-Lou said. He was quite surprised to hear this. "I have been knowing that dude a long time. We even go out and have a drink from time to time. If I had known that, I would have never dealt with you because I don't backtrack on people that I will hang out with." Ny Said".

"You know so many people Luther and the thought came to my mind that you might know him too. So I wasn't going to tell you, and I made sure we stayed away from that place until I got my hooks in you. It's too late now, isn't it, dude? I got this. Don't play." Ny said and kissed The-Lou on his forehead.

"I have fallen in love with you. I want to marry you. Yes, it's too late." The-Lou said. He was getting surrounded by Ny's love and aura. He couldn't bear the thought of leaving her.

"Remember, I always said you jump ahead of the line. It will be guys seeing me with you, telling me that they thought they were going to be next in line?" Ny said.

"Did you fuck them too?" The-Lou asked, expecting to hear a no in return.

"Some of them, but I only do one man at a time, and you are the only one getting this. That's why David had to go." Ny told him. OK

"Call me and let me know that you made it home. Goodbye!" The-Lou said.

XIV

❧ Inside The-Lou's House

Johnnie, The-Lou, and Will-die are sitting at the kitchen table.

"Hey cousin, if you want something done about this, let me know. I can take care of it tomorrow and be back on the plane to Houston, and they will never know what happened. Don't nobody know me here, and if the police don't catch you on the spot, chances are they never will because we all know they don't spend a lot of time investigating black-on-black crimes." Johnnie said.

"Look here, cousin, that African isn't no problem with Luther. All he wanted was his watch," Will-Die said.

"Thanks for having my back, cousin, but my brother is right. I got an understanding with Ny, and she is going give him back everything she can think of, and that's going to be the end of it." The-Lou said.

"I'm leaving in the morning, as you know, but I'm going to leave you with this little brother; you better watch that bitch, because Ny and that gal she was with knew what they were doing. Ain't no real woman is going to go someplace with her man where she knows another mother fucker she used to mess around with is going to be there. And she knows he's looking for her. Just like I heard you say, she told you other guys she was dealing with were talking about getting with him. She was hoping it would be us, but you played that just right. And keep in mind, if she feels that way about him. One day she may feel that way about you." Will-Die said and stood up to leave.

"Now that you broke it down like that cousin, it makes a lot of sense. Now far as Ny goes. Fuck that bitch! HA! HA!" Johnnie said and laughed in an evil way.

ॐ Inside St. Louis Nites Night Club

The-Lou is walking in with Bobby and K-Dog. The-Lou sees David and starts talking to him.

"Hey, man! I had no idea you were messing around with Ny. If I had known that, I would have never dealt with her." The-Lou said to David. He tried his best to keep things under control.

"I know. It isn't your fault. I asked her about you, and she said you were just like a brother to her, but I know now that she is a lying ass bitch. She always told me to keep my mouth shut if I wanted to see her. So that's what I did. Now looking back on it, I should have told you. I didn't find out it was you, until one day I called her and she said: "She was waiting on her man to come to pick her up." I heard her son yell out in the background that Luther was here, and that's when I knew. Until that time, she had me thinking her man was that African dude. But when she came across you and the way you are putting it down with the house, Jaguar, and good job, she thought she may be able to get something out of you because I gave her everything I had to offer, but when it ran out, she ran to you and made it her business that I would never see you and her together again." David told The-Lou everything.

"You're right! Because every time I wanted to come down here with her, she never wanted to come. One time I asked her why she never wanted to go to St. Louis Nites with me. Ny said," That it was a guy that works there she used to see." I would ask her what his name was, but she would never tell me. Here is her reason for not telling me this guy's name. Ny said, "Because you really don't know him, and he only knows of you and I don't want you talking to him and getting some shit started. I don't talk to him anymore, and he's mad because I'm with you and not him, and I want you to think about this, Luther; How many men working at St. Louis Nites told you that I'm seeing him,".

The-Lou said" none." Then Ny said, "If it was somebody you knew, don't you think that they would tell you that they were seeing me if they knew that I saw you." I said, "Okay," and left it at that. The-Lou said.

"That's because she knows that I knew you. Remember! She told me that you're like a brother to her. I'm supposed to keep my mouth shut. Right! I bet she never mentioned my name once, did she?" David said, trying to connect the dots.

"No, she didn't. Now to her credit, that was the first and only time that we came in here together, and that was our first time going out. We were not a couple then, So how did she know we knew each other? The-Lou said. He was quite confident that Ny didn't know about The-Lou and David knowing each other.

"One time, Luther, you spoke to me, and Ny was standing right next to me. When you left, she said that dude is always drunk, and he tries to talk to me every time he sees me, but he never remembers me."

"She told me that, too," The-Lou said.

"I have been in this club business for a while, and one thing I'm going to tell you is that when a person is drunk, and you do be getting your drink on Luther, it's going to be hard to remember somebody if you don't know them," David replied.

"And a woman like Ny you will never recognize because she always looks different every time you see her. Wearing those long eyelashes, she has a wig in every color, blue, blond, gold, red, white, burgundy, and sometimes they are long and straight, short and full, medium straight or full, and if you don't know the person and if you're drunk, you will never recognize them especially if you don't see them all the time."

"What you say makes sense, but I'm in deep now," The-Lou said. He told David that he had completely fallen in love with Ny.

"I understand, but take a word from me. Ny is no good!" David warned The-Lou, advising him to stay away from her. The-Lou nods and shakes David's hand, and walks into the club, followed by K-dog and Bobby.

"I heard that shit David was talking, and Ny is right! When she told you, that mother fucker is mad because he isn't getting that pussy no more. And you can't blame her for wanting to go to something that's bigger and better." K-Dog said.

"Then how come she wouldn't tell me his name?" The-Lou asked.

"If she would have told you who he was? Would you have gotten with her?" K-Dog came up with a question for The-Lou as well.

"No!" The-Lou said.

"K-Dog is right! You can't blame anybody for wanting the best for themselves. It isn't like you talk to him every day or you all go out kickin' it on a regular basis like we do. So fuck it. You got a pretty fine woman, and she seems like she loves you, and what a person does in their past has nothing to do with the way they treat you now! You are happy with this woman Luther, so enjoy it." Bobby said, convincing The-Lou that Ny is the lane that leads to his happiness, so he must ignore the past and all that she did previously in her life.

"Damn right! Because if Ny acted like she was going to come over to his house right now! I bet he would come up with an excuse to leave work and go and get that pussy. Come on! Let's get a drink and get on some of these hoes." K-Dog said". He knew how much The-Lou loved that woman and would do anything just to be with her.

❧ Inside The-Lou's House-4 Months Later

The phone rings. The-Lou answers it, and it's Will-Die on the other side.

"What's going on, little brother? How are you and that dame doing?"

"It's funny that you would ask that. We have been doing fine up until a month ago, when she got Her new job at the water Company "What's wrong?" Will-Die asked as The-Lou sounded quite gloomy.

"It started around my birthday. I wanted to see the Da-Lahoya fight, and she raised hell that she didn't want to see a fight; it was my birthday, but she never had a problem watching the fights this summer. One week after that, she came over to my house unannounced and told me she was going to kick my ass if I had some bitch in there. Three Sunday's ago. I had one of my partners from New York come thru and a few of the other fellas. I called Ny on the phone and asked her to stop by. She said" that she had something to do and couldn't make it." Then for no reason, it just started going off. I said a few things while talking to my boys and didn't hang up the phone. She overheard what I said. The next thing I know, she comes charging in my house talking bad to me in front of my friends, and she did it again when my dog Benny O was over."

"You sound like you're getting a soft little brother. I remember the times when you would tell a bitch, to kiss your ass in a minute."

"I am in love with this woman, I want to marry her, and if I plan on being married, I have to learn how to take the good with the bad. She was out of work this summer, but now she has a job, and it seems like her attitude has changed. She said,"

She was going to marry me, but she wanted to buy her own house because she didn't like the schools in my neighborhood," and my hood is better than anyone she's ever lived in. Then one day, she called me, and I didn't hear the phone ring. I called her back ten minutes later, and she cursed me out and told me to keep on fuckin that bitch I am with. One other time she started cursing at me because I wouldn't stop and get a pair of cheap earrings. Ny told me she was going to fuck the night up if I didn't get those earrings. Another time she called, and my cell phone battery went dead, and she left all of these nasty messages on my voicemail. I was on the east side, and I was too tired to make it home, so I spent the night over at my mother's house. When I got back home, she parked her car in my garage. And I could not put the Jag in there. Hold on! Let me get to the other end. Hey brother, this is her now. Let me call you back." The-Lou said.

"Hey, did you check on the truck yet?" Ny asked.

"Yes, but I'm not like you. If I say I'm going to do something, I will do it. I am still waiting on my shoes for my birthday.

"Once I get to move in. I will give you the rest of the money for your shoes on Christmas. I have got to go; call me back later, baby. Goodbye!" Ny said and bid him goodbye.

❧ Inside Benny O's House

Benny O and The-Lou are sitting down drinking Cognac.

"Luther, you are my boy, and we go way back. But I am going to tell you, man,

I will help you move this bitch, but you complain about her so much. I bet you a fifth of Cognac 2 weeks after we get Ny to move into her house. You will be complaining about her again. Out of all the women you had, she is the only one I don't like." Benny O said to "The-Lou".

6 Days before Ny is supposed to move, The-Lou is on the phone trying to call Ny, and she is not answering. It's now 12:30 am, and The-Lou hasn't heard from Ny all day.

The-Lou is really pissed off now. He goes over to Pep's house, and they are drinking beer, and Yhe-Lou is upset about not hearing from Ny.

"Where do you think she is?" Pep asked The-Lou. He was quite worried about Ny too.

"I don't know, but now I am starting to think another man is involved," The-Lou said.

"Why would you say that?" Pep asked The-Lou. He didn't like to see him upset.

"She has been starting a whole lot of shit with me for no reason. I will tell you this, I'm getting ready to go over to her house, and it's going to be about 1:00 am when I get there. If Ny's son answers the door and tells me she is not there, we are going to have a big problem like, I'm not going to help her move." The-Lou said. He was quite pissed off and didn't know how to react.

⊰ Outside Of Ny's House

The-Lou doesn't see Ni's car. The-Lou knocks on the door, and Jr. answers the door.

"Hey Luther! What's up?" Jr said.

"Has your mother called and said where she was at?" The-Lou asked Jr. He was furious but controlled his tone here.

"I haven't heard or seen her all day," Jr. replied.

"Tell her to call me as soon as she gets in. It's about me helping her move."

The-Lou said and left. He was quite furious and had no idea where the hell Ny was. He sits in his car and drives away to Pep's place.

⊰ Inside Pep's House

The-Lou is on his cell phone calling Ny, but no answer. He is quite upset and angry and wants to have a word with Ny at any cost.

"Fuck that bitch! It's 2:00 am, and I haven't heard from her. The bad thing about it, she has her son lying to her. He said, "he haven't seen or heard from his mother all day," and I know that's a lie. Every time I'm with Ny, she always calls to check on Jr. If nothing else, she is going to keep in contact with her son. I don't fault him. He is just doing what his mother tells him to do. So this is what I'm going to do. I'm not going to help that bitch move, and I'm going to cancel the truck." The-Lou said. He was quite frustrated.

"If you cancel the truck, you will never see her again." Pep reminded The-Lou about the consequences of canceling the truck.

"Ny can carry that shit on her back and get that punk ass man she with right now to help her," The-Lou replied. He was getting frustrated and really wanted to get in touch with Ny.

"You're just mad now, Luther. You don't have to help her move, but you should let her keep the truck." Pep said, keeping a hand on his shoulder.

"I don't know. I will think about it," The-Lou said. It's 6:15 am. The-Lou's phone rings, and he shows Pep on his caller I.D. that it's Ny. The-Lou answers.

"So, where in the hell have you been?" The-Lou said as soon as he received the call. He was quite mad at Ny for not talking to him for a whole day.

"I was with Keyana, the girl I used to work with. My cell phone went dead, and she doesn't have a house phone, so I couldn't call. Plus, I had too much to drink."

Ny told The-Lou about where she was.

"That's bullshit! I've been with you long enough to know that you don't drink too much. I never heard of this friend you just made up, and you always check on your son 5 or 6 times a night when we are together, but he says he hasn't heard from you all day. Just like you told me to keep on fucking that bitch I'm with when I didn't answer my phone in ten minutes. Well, you get that mother fucker you were with tonight to help you move. I had 14 of my partners ready to help you move. We would have been out of the old house and in your new house in a couple of hours. But you just fuck that up! And I was getting ready to turn the truck back in. But Pep, talk me out of that. So the next time you see him. Thank him. Because I don't want to see your lying bitch ass again, and don't call me!" The-Lou said all he wanted to say in a single breath and hung up the phone. He didn't believe a word Ny had said and was quite confident that she was lying this time as well.

"Kind of hard on her, wasn't you?" Pep said.

"Not hard enough, Thanks to you, I let her keep the truck," The-Lou said.

❧ Inside St. Louis

Nites and its been a couple of days since The-Lou has talk to Ny.

The-Lou, Bobby, and K-Dog are sitting at the table having a drink.

"Hey fellas, I am not going to help Ny move, so don't worry about Saturday,"

The-Lou told everybody about their breakup and that he would never see Ny's face ever.

"Are you sure!" K-Dog asked him to make sure whether he meant it all or not.

"Damn right! I know there is another man involved. I just don't know who it could be. I'm going to tell you all something, if you all see Ny getting her ass kicked by some man, please don't get in it." The-Lou said he was certain that she was dating two men and was cheating on him for sure.

"Now you know if we see somebody beating her down, we are going to do something," Bobby said.

"No, I mean it! Anytime someone is always accusing you of messing around, they are the one's doing it. Then want to start bullshit arguments for no reason. And you know, you're doing the right things." The-Lou replied.

"Well, you got a point there because people will try to make you think you're the one messing up when it's them all the time. That's one of the oldest tricks in the book." K-Dog said.

"Hey fellas, I'm not going to be here too long. I'm waiting on this gal to call me, and when she does, I'm up." The-Lou replied.

"Damn, brother, I see that you are serious. I haven't heard you talk about another woman. It seems like, in almost a year." Bobby said.

"A man got to do! What a man got to do!" The-Lou replied.

The-Lou, Bobby, and K-Dog are sitting at the table, and from out of nowhere, Ny pulls up a seat next to The-Lou. Bobby and K-Dog are shocked to see her. The-Lou looked at Ny really hard. Then said, "Get the hell away from me now"! Ny takes off her coat and leaves it on the chair, then walks off. Bobby and K-Dog go over to talk to Ny.

K-Dog came back to the table and said "I have been listing to Ny, and to me, she sounds like she is telling the truth"

The-Lou wasn't hearing it. Bobby came over to talk to The-Lou, and he wasn't listening to him either. Thirty minutes went by, and The-Lou was looking at his phone to see if that girl called. Bobby came back to the table with Ny and sat her down next to The-Lou.

"I really believe this girl loves you, man! Come on, and you all work this out." Bobby said, trying to convince The-Lou not to give up on his woman this easily.

Ny held The-Lou's hand. Then she took her hand and put it on the side of his face and turned it towards hers, and then she kissed him. The-Lou was back in love again. He went home with Ny that night. The next day, he called everybody back and told them its back on to help Ny move. When he called Benny O, he started going off.

"What! It's back on! You said that you would have 13 or 14 of your boys that were going to help Ny move. Are they still going to do it?" Benny O said.

"Yeah!" The-Lou said "You got some people out there that love your ass. Going back and forth like that. Plus, it's not you that's moving, but your woman and you're paying us nothing either, and it's on a Saturday when most of us are off and want to relax. But you know I'm here for you, dog, and remember our bet. A fifth of Cognac because it won't be two weeks before you start raising hell about her again." Said Benny O to The-Lou.

Despite the repeated betrayals, remained deeply in love with Ny. He couldn't resist her charm, her infectious laughter, and the way she made him feel alive. Each time she broke his heart, he would retreat into himself for a while, but eventually, his love for her would pull him back in. It was a never-ending cycle, and he knew he was setting himself up for more heartbreak, but he couldn't help it. His love for her was like an addiction that he couldn't shake off. Deep down, he hoped that one day, Ny would realize his worth and stop hurting him. Until then, he would continue to give her chances, hoping that things would eventually work out between them.

XV

$\mathcal{N}$y and The-Lou were happy in their relationship. Despite the happiness in their relationship, Ny couldn't resist the temptation of sleeping with other guys in town.

She knew it was wrong and that it would hurt The-Lou, but she didn't care at all. She tried to justify her actions by telling herself that The-Lou would never find out. Almost every other man in the town knew about Ny's fat ass and juicy pussy, but The-Lou was all blind in love.

❧ Inside Benny O House

The-Lou comes walking in with a fifth of Cognac.

"Didn't I tell you? Didn't I tell you, dog? Shid!!! Hell! Now that I think about it, it was less than one week. HA! HA! Tell me what happened again. I didn't get all of the story." Benny O said, laughing out loud.

"My brother Will-Die was in town. So Ny, he, and I went on the boat to eat crab legs. On the way back home, I bought her a cup of ice for 10 cents. We parked in her driveway because she was supposed to go out with us. I was a little thirsty, and I drank the water from when the ice melted. She started screaming and yelling, then snatched the cup right out of my mouth and told me don't be drinking her damn water. Then she said," I am mad; I'm not going anywhere tonight! I am going to stay in my house and read my bible" She got out of the car and slammed the door, and then went into her house." The-Lou said.

"Now you know that's bullshit! What in the hell is she going to get mad about? You're the one who spends 10 cents on the ice. HA! HA!" Benny O replied. He was quite in a funny mode that day.

"Now I am convinced it's some other man. I just don't know who?" I The Lou said, telling Benny O about his confusion.

"So what are you going to do?" Benny O asked him. He wanted to know if there was any way he could help The-Lou.

"Play it for what it's worth. If I come across a woman I want to be with, now I'm going to get with her." The-Lou said.

It was Christmas day, and Ny didn't get The-Lou's shoes, but he gave her some really nice gifts, including a leather coat. The only thing she gave him was a cheap St. Louis Rams jacket he had seen on sale at the mall for $60.00. Ny said " she didn't have any money," But her son looked like he got everything he wanted, not to mention she went and bought a T.V and had a big screen T.V. fixed for $500.00, but The-Lou didn't care because he was really in love with Ny. The next day, Ny had The-Lou go to Doug's furniture store with her to pick up her rocking chair. The-Lou starts thinking.

"You got money to spend on this chair but couldn't get my shoes?" The-Lou asked Ny; he was quite disappointed in her.

"I put some furniture in the lay-a-way in June. But I'm not going to have enough money to get it out. They would not give me my money back, so I took this." Ny told him what the scene was exactly.

"How come they wouldn't give you your money back?" The-Lou asked Ny.

"Because I sign my name Ny Hines instead of Nigeria Hines. And I didn't have my receipt, so they told me that I couldn't have the money back, but I could get $300.00 worth of furniture." Ny told him the entire thing about why she wasn't getting any money back.

"That's bullshit! Where is the manager at?" The-Lou" said. |He was quite furious and wanted to talk to or meet the manager immediately.

"Come on! We ain't got time for that. I need to get back home so I can drop Jr. off at the movies with the rest of his friends." Ny said out of frustration.

❧ Inside The-Lou's House

The-Lou is lying across the bed watching T.V. The phone rings, and it's Ny. They make plans to go to the movies at 7:00 pm. The-Lou is dressed and waiting on Ny, but she never comes. He calls her cell phone, and there is no answer. 11:45 pm The-Lou is mad.

The phone rings, and it's Ny.

"Where in the hell are you, and why did you stand me up like this?" The-Lou asked Ny furiously.

"I thought I called you and said I was going out with Stacy," Ny replied.

"You know damn well you didn't call me and tell me that!" The-Lou angrily said.

Sometimes he couldn't understand what Ny was actually up to.

"I'm telling you now! I'm out!" Ny answered in a quite frustrated manner.

"So, are you coming over here?" The-Lou asked, trying to lower his tone and keep calm.

"I will call you when I get ready to leave," Ny said and hung up the phone.

The-Lou disconnected the call and waited to hear back from Ny. But unfortunately, he didn't hear from Ny until the next morning. The-Lou calls Ny on the phone.

"What happened to you last night?" The-Lou asked Ny, waiting to hear the excuse she was ready to give him.

"I saw the car parked in front of your house last night, so I know you had some bitch in there, so keep on doing what you are doing with that hoe?" Ny questioned The-Lou instead of answering his questions.

That's bullshit! I remember when you would come over to my house without calling, knocking on my door, talking about you going to kick my ass if I got some damn bitch in there. Now you think that I would have one in here, and you just drive on by. Let me tell you something; don't you insult my intelligence." The-Lou said, trying his best to get the blame off his shoulders because he knew there was no one in his place last night.

"Hey! Look! Let's just forget about it. Will I see you today?" The-Lou continued.

He wanted to meet Ny.

"I just told your ass to get with that bitch that you were with last night," Ny said; she was furious and wouldn't let The-Lou speak.

"Hey! Fuck you! I don't take this shit off of nobody!" The-Lou said and hung up the phone.

The-Lou has now started seeing other women, and Ny has no idea that's what he is doing. But it's not the same for him. When The-Lou is with another woman, whether he is making love to her or not, he still finds himself thinking about Ny. The-Lou realizes that he is more in love with Ny than he thought. When you can't stop thinking about someone, you're in love with them. So The-Lou stop seeing other Women and just concentrated on Ny. There would be good day and there would be bad days but this relationship, heart ship is starting to take a toll on The-Lou, plus he is starting not to look like his usual self. Everything was fine for about three weeks, but then Ny started acting crazy again. One day they were going over to The-Lou's cousin's house. The-Lou mentioned an ex-girlfriend, and Ny went crazy. She said," If you want that bitch go and get her and take me home" But Ny could talk about her ex-boyfriends, and it's okay. The following week, Ny and The-Lou were going to a party, and Ny started the same old stuff again. They made it through the night, and when they woke up in the morning, The-Lou made it his business to go to church with Ny because she says it's his fault that she is not getting her blessing from God.

Because he keeps her up late on Saturday night bar hopping, and she can't get up and go to church.

❧ Inside The Church

The-Lou and Ny sat down in the church pews, listening intently to the preacher's words. The sermon was about forgiveness, and The-Lou felt a pang in his heart as he thought about Ny's infidelity. He wondered if he was capable of forgiving her and moving past the pain. As the preacher finished his sermon, The-Lou and Ny exchanged a knowing glance. They both knew that they had a long way to go, but the words of the preacher gave them a glimmer of hope that their love could overcome the hurt and pain.

"There are something's out here that people should not be doing, and one of them is levitating. That means taking care of business. Don't be late for work, do what you are supposed to do. Another thing is fornication." The preacher said.

"Did you hear that? Did you hear that? Well! Did you?" Ny asked The-Lou looking at him to make sure he was listening to it all with concentration.

The-Lou nodded absentmindedly, still lost in thought about the preacher's sermon.

As they left the church and made their way back home, he was unaware of what Ny had planned next. Little did he know that she was already making plans to break his heart once again.

❧ Inside Ny's House

Ny is going thru her closet and pulling out The-Lou's clothes. She looked quite tensed and was preparing for him to leave the place.

"You are going to have to leave," Ny said, turning to The-Lou. She didn't tell him the reason, though.

"What in the hell is wrong now!" The-Lou asked out of irritation.

"You heard the Preacher, don't be fornicating," Ny replied.

"Well, let's get married! How many times have I asked you? And you are always complaining about money. If you had married me, you would be in a house twice the size of yours, in a brand new car, plus the ones I have, and money in your pocket." The-Lou said. He had all the things Ny could ever want in her life.

"I can't marry you, Luther, because you're missing the main ingredient," Ny answered.

"Oh, I see! You're looking for Cuba Gooding Sr. because he is the lead singer for The Main Ingredient. What in the fuck are you talking about? You don't want to see me anymore?" The-Lou asked. He was quite pissed off by Ny's answer.

"No! I didn't say that. I said we won't be having sex anymore, and you will not be spending any nights over here, and I won't be spending any nights over there." Ny said. It was clear that she was avoiding The-Lou, but the reason was unknown.

"You will not marry me, you will not have sex with me, and we can't spend the night with each other no more, so I take it that I'm not your man anymore," The-Lou said. He was shattered hearing these words from Ny.

"You said that I didn't," Ny replied, being as rude and ruthless as she could.

"What kind of woman are you going to be if I can't make love to you? I said that I would marry you, but you have a problem with that. And the reason you just gave me lets me know that you don't think shit about me. Just tell me anything. But if you want me to go, then I'll leave." The-Lou said and left Ny's house.

The-Lou made up in mind he was going to play it real cool and let Ny come to him, so he never called once he left with his belonging and gave her back the door key. Three weeks later, Ny calls The-Lou from her job at the water company. Ny tells The-Lou that she is seeing a guy that she met at a church, and they are on the same religious page. They don't have sex; all they do is go to the show and out to dinner. This not what The-Lou expected to hear. He thought she was going to want him back. Plus she said they study the bible together. Ny tells The-Lou that his name is Ralph Ledbelly, and he is 57 years old and 5 feet and 2 inches, with a bald head, and weighs 210 pounds.

"Come over to my house and talk to me about this shit in person," The-Lou said and told her to see him tonight at dinner. They would discuss it all.

※ Inside The-Lou's House

Ny is sitting on the sofa with a big grin on her face. The-Lou doesn't look happy at all. There was a lot going on in his mind at that moment.

"I want you to know that I still do love you, and I want us to remain friends," Ny said, looking at The-Lou.

"So, when did you start seeing him?" The-Lou asked her. He wanted to know everything about the man Ny was dating.

"When you got mad and left," Ny replied.

"I didn't get mad and leave. You told me to go, remember, because we can't have sex and spend the night with each other! And what's so good about Grandpa?"

The-Lou reminded her of what actually happened. He wasn't expecting this type of attitude from Ny.

"Well, he deposits his whole check in my bank account, and you wouldn't do that," Ny replied. She was getting greedier each day.

"No, I just offered you my house, car, and everything else I own. If you would have married me." The-Lou scoffed and said. He reminded Ny how much he loved her.

"Well, he is just like me! We are both trying to hear from God, and you know what! He heard from him, and God told him that I was going to be his wife, but at first, he told God no, but God said yes! And that I am going to be his wife." Ny told The-Lou all about it, ignoring what The-Lou was saying. She was too much intoxicated by greed and money at that time,

"Do you hear how you sound? You must think I'm crazy, or you've just lost your fucking mind!" The-Lou said as he heard what Ny was saying. It did not even make sense. The-Lou scoffed and nodded his head.

"You see! You see! That, there, is just what I'm talking about. That ain't nothing but the devil." Ny said, pointing out The-Lou's reaction and proving that he was just overreacting.

"Why don't you come back later on tonight? I gotta make a move." The-Lou said as he got up to leave. He had had enough of Ny's shit, and now she wasn't even making any sense.

"Where are you going?" Ny asked as she saw him getting up.

"Running with the devil. I will see you later." The-Lou replied sarcastically.

Ny came back over that night. When she walked in, The-Lou didn't say much to her; he just grabbed her hand and took her upstairs to his bedroom, undressed her, and made love to her. It had been almost a month since the last time The-Lou saw Ny, and he was missing her but when he made love to her, and then, all of his feeling for her came back stronger than ever.

"Can we please stop all of this fucking around and get married," The-Lou said. He couldn't lose her. He was madly in love with her. The next day when they wake up, The-Lou hands Ny a bible. She opens it up, and there is $2,000.00 for an engagement ring; then he hands her the keys to his house and cars. Ny looks at it for a minute, then hands it back to him.

"I can't marry you, Luther; you don't have the main ingredient yet," Ny said. She constantly keeps on mentioning the main ingredients missing in The-Lou.

"Almost a month ago, you said we wouldn't have sex anymore. Now correct me if I'm wrong, but didn't we just do that? Now, isn't that the reason why I had to leave in the first damn place." The-Lou said. He wanted to convince Ny the time is now to finally get married to him.

"I have my needs, but I'm still waiting to hear from God." Ny laughed and The-Lou just shook his head in discuss. The-Lou and Ny are seeing each other again but Ny told The-Lou she is not going to stop seeing Ralph. He didn't care because he was an old fat religious man and he believes that Ny would come back and they would be the way they were.

A thought came to The-Lou, the reason Ny will not marry him is because she wants a man to pay for her lifestyle and she can still do whatever she wants, some men would put up with that but she knew if she marry The-Lou, he wouldn't go for it.

Inside Two Brothers Club

A couple of days later. The-Lou goes to meet Pep for a drink during happy hour. Pep is sitting with some guys he knows. Pep introduces everybody, and one of the guys knows who The-Lou is, and Ny too. One of Pep's friends told The-Lou that he had seen Ny out at Doug's Furniture with some man, and they were acting like they were a couple. The-Lou then thinks about the chair and the bullshit line that Ny told him. The-Lou asked the bartender for the phone book. The-Lou called Doug's Furniture and asked them if they had the kind of policy that Ny told him. The manager told him no! He said" that they would keep $50.00 a month for as long as the furniture is in the lay-a-way. No matter how they sign it, you got to have a receipt and I.D. before you can get a refund or take any merchandise out of the store because if that were the case, anybody off the streets can come up and say that they are this person and do you think we are going to give it to them if they can't prove it". The-Lou thank the man for his time. He is positive that Ny had been messing around, he just wonders who it is. The-Lou asked Pep's friend what the guy looked like. He said "kind of tall, skinny, light skin brother." The-Lou left in a hurry. Pep friend said your boy Lou ain't looking to good these day. Pep replied' yea! That woman you seen at Doug's is driving him crazy The-Lou immediately called Ny and asked her who was the light skin skinny dude she was with at Doug's Furniture store, Pep friend told me he saw you." The-Lou said .

"Who? Jr," Ny asked The-Lou. She was now in hot water for sure.

"You know damn well it wasn't Jr. Now I know where that chair came from.

I called the people at Doug's, and they said they don't have a policy like that. You are one lying ass woman. Ny said "Oh! I know who you are talking about, that was I guy I use to work with, he always trying to hit on me, that why it may have looked like I was with him. The-Lou said " yea Ok."

The-Lou is in Country Lake Park, and the club owners of Mrs. Wicks are throwing a big bash. The-Lou's phone rings, and it's Benny O.

"What's up, dog? I've been kicking it down here in Dallas! What's going on with you?" Benny O said.

"Ny came over the other night, and we did our thing in the bedroom, but I don't know what to think about her. I still am madly in love with her, but I might just need to leave her alone because of the lies and talking all that crazy, religious fanatic shit that she is a big-time hypocrite on. But I am in love with this woman. What do you think?" The-Lou told Benny what was troubling him. He wasn't sure what to do and what not to do.

"Well, I wasn't going to say anything, but you asked, so I got to tell you, dog. I saw Ny Friday at the QT, and she was shocked as hell to see me in there because she was with some dude. She told me his name was Ralph and that they were going on some kind of trip." Benny O told The-Lou .

"Yeah, she told me about some old mother fucker she met at church named Ralph she hangs out with. Ain't he bald, 5ft 2in, weight about 210 pounds, and looks like he is 67 years old?"

"Hell naw! This dude looks like he could be 35, maybe 40. about 6ft. and skinny. Hey Luther, if that is who she is fucking around with, and remember you asked me. I will let her ass go. That dude she with ain't got nothing on you. If she put you down, so she can get with that nigga, and he is a little dusty, and that car they were riding in should not be allowed on the road. Ny is poison, leave her alone, and that is the advice you asked for." Benny O said. He was quite certain that Ny wasn't the right lady for The-Lou. If she stays in his life, she can be a tremendous disaster in his life.

"One of Pep's partners saw Ny about two months ago at Doug's and described the same dude. Hey brother, I will get back to you. I got some thinking to do."

It's Sunday, and The-Lou is in church. The cell phone rings, and it's Ny. The-lou leaves the church, and he's talking to Ny, and he is upset.

"Well, how was your trip?" The-Lou asked Ny. Though Ny didn't tell him anything about going on a trip, he still bothered to ask.

"Oh, it was nice," Ny said. She didn't even bother to ask how did The-Lou come to know about the trip or anything else.

"You know that Benny O was going to tell me he saw you. How can you let that mother fucker spend the night, but I can't?" The-Lou asked her. He was burning out of anger and jealousy. Ny was all over his mind, and he couldn't understand what the hell was going on in his life.

"He doesn't spend the night?" Ny asked him.

"Ny, Jay is not the only one I work with that lives in that neighborhood, and that piece of the shit car is parked in front of your house too early in the morning for him not to be spending the night," The-Lou said, trying to explain to Ny that she might get herself in some serious trouble.

"Sometimes he comes over at 2:00 am, and we play games," Ny said; she still considered lying to The-Lou.

"What games? Name that damn preacher! And why lie about what he looks like?" The-Lou asked her, frustrated and wanting final answers to his questions.

"Because I told you, don't ask me about my business. If you don't ask me, then I won't lie. But now that you know, I want you to meet him. He is really nice, and he is going to be a preacher." Ny said.

"What! Fuck him! I don't want to meet his ass. For what! What do you want? A damn threesome!" The-Lou yelled. He couldn't believe what his ears were hearing.

"I told you we don't have sex," Ny said, trying to play innocent and playful.

"Ny, ain't no man alive is going to give you his whole check, and his car will be parked outside your house at 5:00 in the morning if you're not giving him any pussy. And you're going on trips with him. What happened? How did this happen? I was going to take the equity out of my house and go buy one of those Kensington's for us." The-Lou said. He was surely in love with her, but this was way too far.

"Well, you just take your equity and find another woman and move the fuck on, and don't worry about me no more," Ny replied with a really nasty attitude.

"Fuck you bitch! You fucking hoe! You lying ass mother fuckin bitch! I fuckin hate your ass. Don't you ever speak to me again, and if you see me, you better not say one mother fuckin word to me, do you hear me bitch. Fuck you and him! Bitch!" The-Lou replied in a rage of anger.

Ny is riding with Paula, and Paula grabs the phone.

"I can hear you from where I'm sitting. Calm down; you might want her back. The-Lou Said" One other thing Paula. You knew how long Ny was dealing with Ralph, but you never once told me what was going on. I understand you're more of her friend than mine, so I have no problem with that, but the next time you call me, don't talk to me about Ny and how she feels because I don't believe the shit she has to say. Because if you were going to tell me anything? It should have been about what I needed to know about her seeing Ralph. But you didn't tell me anything when I told you about how badly she was messing up. You knew she was seeing Ralph, but you let me help her move anyway, knowing that woman was making a fool out of me. So that being said.

I don't believe anything you say either when it comes to Ny. So the next time we talk, don't bring her damn name up! Later." pain The-Lou felt knowing that Ny is in bed with another Man is tearing him apart, for almost a month he couldn't sleep and couldn't eat, because his worse fears of her having another man turn out to be true.

A few days later The-Lou is on his mom's front porch with his brother Will-Die and his cousin Nate. The-Lou is talking to his Mother about Ny, he is drowning his sorrows to her like he has been with everyone else. The-Lou Mom starts crying. She said "Luther! I have never seen you like this, look at you. Your hair looks a hot mess, not clean shaven, your shirt and pants are all wrinkle, shoe's look like they came from the Goodwill. Come here let me smell you. The-Lou Mom grabs him and brings him close to her and she said "well at least you don't stink! This Woman has driven you crazy and everyone can see it but you. Nate said "You may not stink but you sho look like you do" then he starts laughing. Will-Die said "Mom is right! You use to be so fly, now if I didn't know you, I would walk up to you and give you a Quarter". Then he and Nate start laughing. The-Lou Mom said "that's not funny, this boy is in some serious pain". Nate said "Well if he keeps this up, he better get use to it, because if we are laughing and we are family, just think what the people on the streets are saying about you and believe me, it ain't nothing good. The-Lou's Mom with tears in her eyes said "I remember when women would come over here crying to me about you, now you're the one pain, so please tell how does it feel heartbreaker? The-Lou hears them but he is so distraught about Ny, it's not sinking in.

The-Lou is at work, and a lot of his co-workers, Bruce, Keith, Donald, and Jay, are talking to The-lou, and all of them live in Ny's neighborhood, and Jay lives right next door to Ny.

"Where have you been, dude? I don't see you no more, just some other guy that's coming over there now." Jay asked The-Lou as he saw him.

"She broke up with me talking about religion when I know it's about the Money and control," The-Lou replied.

"He's right! I came over to your house one day, Jay and you were not home, and he was pulling up in. I don't know what the fuck that is; he's driving. Hell, I'm surprised that the state would let him put a license plate on that mother fucker. But anyway, when he got out of the car, that dude looked like he hadn't had a bath in 25 years." Bruce said.

"They always say you can tell what kind of man you have by the car he is driving. HA! HA! Keith said. With this, he started laughing.

"That's right! Because I don't know which one of them was more fuck up, him or the car? And that car is fuck up! I see cars come out looking better than that after a smash, crash, derby race." Bruce said.

"You said he looks like he doesn't bathe if he's that funky, The-Lou! I bet your ex gal is running around the house saying, are you down with ODB? Yea! You know me! Are you down with ODB? Yea! You know me!" Keith said.

"What's ODB?" Jay asked Keith. He had this term for the first time in his life.

"Old Dirty Bastard. He was a rapper that died." Keith replied.

"Now that I think about it. She can be named after a rapper that's dead too.

Because of all of the stories she tells, instead of THE Notorious B.I.G., we can start calling her The Notorious L.I.E.," The-Lou said out of frustration.

"Luther, I'm going to come to you straight. You wouldn't mind if I tried to get some of that pussy. Because you are right! It's got to be about the money for her to let you go and bring him in there. I'll tell everybody right now. I will buy some of that pussy, and if she will fuck Old Dirty Bastard, then she will fuck anybody if the price is right." Bruce said as this cunning idea popped into his mind.

"I am still in love with that woman, but I have to face reality. And I did everything I could to get that woman to marry me. But she wanted somebody else that she can totally control, this stupid mother fucker puts his whole check in her bank account and that's something I wouldn't do even if I was married. Now back to you Bruce. If it's not him or you, then it will be somebody else. Thanks for being man enough to bring it to me." The-Lou said with a heavy heart.

"The-Lou, I would have never thought twice about it if it had been a regular breakup. Everybody knows you were crazy about that woman, but the way she kicked you to the curve and put a mother fucker like that in your place. And it's not just me, but a whole lot of us have lost respect for her. So, if she fucking dudes like that, she can come over here and give me some of that pussy too." Bruce advised him. He was well aware of what type of woman Ny was and that The-Lou didn't deserve anyone like her.

"Respect means a lot. My son came home and told me that they were giving her son a lot of shit at school about what happened to the Drop Top Jag? I guess it turned back into a pumpkin Cinderella, or no more Jag because they hit hard times.

Now they ride around in a piece of shit because they ain't got a dime." Donald said as he joined the conversation.

"A woman is always talking about that; she wants the best for her kids. But when it comes to money, they don't care and ain't thinking about what kind of man they are bringing into their lives, just as long as they are getting paid. I'm not saying I'm right or wrong, but after listening to what Donald just said. I would bet her son ain't too happy with Luther being gone and ODB in his place." Keith said.

"If you think he ain't happy, you know how I'm feeling," The-Lou replied.

"Just stay up! You got you're shit together, just like you found her, you will find somebody else and maybe even better. The day is going to come when you'll be glad you didn't marry her. You can't do wrong and expect the right to happen."

Donald said he was quite pissed off by the thought The-Lou was eager to marry a hoe like Ny.

The-Lou was having a hard time getting over Ny because he knew it was over. He was drinking every day; then he realized that wasn't helping. Because alcohol just put his problems on hold, and it never did help.

It got to the point that all of his friends and family told him to get over it and don't come around talking about that bitch no more. The only ones who would continue to listen to him talk about Ny were his brother Will-Die and his friend Bobby.

XVI

*I*ts been 2 months since The-Lou has seen Ny and he still hasn't gotten over her. Ny was like an addictive drug he couldn't shake off. Just the thought of another man with her is still driving him crazy, now its very noticeable that he has lost weight. One day Joyce came over and she was crying her eyes out over The-Lou. She said "I really love you Luther ever since we met when we 18 years old. I know I am not your type of Woman. I know I am not that pretty or have the big round booty but I am the best damn woman you ever had and all I ever wanted to show you that I can be a great wife. I want to be Mrs. Bogan. The-Lou mind was still on Ny, then he asked Joyce? What did you say? Joyce look at him, then shook her head in discuss. Then Joyce said "well I see your not paying any attention to what I am saying, so come on, let's go to your bedroom and fuck! The-Lou still not responding. Joyce gets loud "do you hear me Nigga? Joyce now speaking in a slow hard tone voice" Do you want to fuck"? The-Lou said "yea, yea, yea, ok lets go. Its been 3 months now The-Lou is shaping up, he is now well groomed with his hair, clothes and shoe's. He almost back to his regular self. Another month goes by now The-Lou is fully back to being who he was, not giving Ny a 2nd thought until one day the phone rings and its Ny. I guess what they say is true, when things start going good, that's when The Devil steps in. When The-Lou saw her number, his Heart skip a beat. He didn't know if he should answer it or not, then he answer the phone playing it as cool as he could. The-Lou said "Hello stranger" Ny said "Hello! I called to say I am sorry and what happen? How did you let me get away? The-Lou said "If your going to start with this bullshit I will hang up right now"! Ny said' ok, please don't hang up. I think I made a mistake, I am not seeing Ralph anymore. He move out 2 weeks ago and I finally got up the courage to call you". So what do you want with me? The-Lou said. Ny said "I want to work on us, can I please come over later" ? The-Lou said "I will think about it, I am suppose to have a date tonight but it's not confrim". Ny said "ok call me later if you want to see me". She hangs up and The-Lou heart is racing. He calls up his date and told her he wasn't going to be able to make it. Not trying to look so anxious, he waited 3 hours before he called Ny back told her she could come over. Its 8pm and it's Ny come walking thru the door, she is dress really nice with her tight fitting clothes showing every curve from her big round breast, to her small waist line to her curvy hips, big thighs and big round apple bottom butt. She immediately hug The-Lou and gave him a passionate kiss. The-Lou trying to play it cool like it was no big deal but inside the fire was lit. They both had a couple of drinks and discuss taking slow because The-Lou told her he was seeing other women but deep down he knew she was the only one he wanted. Its wasn't long before they made it to the bedroom and soon as they started having sex, just like that The-Lou is hooked all over again. Just like someone on drugs, they can be off of them for a long time but that one hit and they are hook again and Love is no different. Its been a couple of weeks and The-Lou and Ny are seeing each other almost everyday. This is the happiest The-Lou has been. He is now starting to tell people that he and Ny are back to gather and that didn't sit well with some of his friends and family.

Most of them told The-Lou to stay away from her because she was no good. Some of them said, "If she wants to come back, then let her. Just fuck her! Get her money, and that niggas too. No one thought it was good thing that they were seeing each other again. Some good advice came from Bobby.

"Hey! You are a grown man. And you know what you want better than anybody else out here. She dogs you out emotionally, but if you think that she has changed, then try to work it out. But I am going to tell you the truth, and you remember this The-Lou. If a dog will bite your ass once, she will bite your ass again. So be careful." Bobby said to The-Lou. The-Lou goes over Benny O's house and tells him that he is seeing Ny again. Benny O looks at him like he is crazy then he said "Ny is poison and she has shown on more than one occasion she is no good! All I can say is that I hope I never get any pussy that is that damn good. Best of luck to you brother and your going to need it because dealing with her, your luck is going to be all bad.

The-Lou pulls up in front of his mother's house. She is sitting on the front porch with his brother Will-Die and his cousin Nate is over there again. The-Lou goes and has a seat next to them.

He tells them what's been going on with him and Ny. Will-Die is shaking his head.

The-Lou's Mom said "I'm going to tell you something, son. That girl ran you crazy and if you get back involved with her. You know how bad you felt the first time if she does the same thing again and she will. It's going to be even worse the second time around. Then The-Lou Mom starts crying and she saidYou will go right over the edge Luther and there is a good possibility that you will end up dead or in Jail over a woman that has shown you time and time again she don't love you. You are a grown man, and if you think she has changed, then, by all means, go for it."

The-Lou's mom said in a sarcastic, angry voice "I don't know, Ny; I've only seen her once, maybe twice, so I can't say much about her. The only thing I can go on is what you tell me, and most of it was not good. But I told you! That she was not going to marry you if she wanted to buy her own house. Here you are! Big ass house with an in-ground swimming pool; you got it completely furnished from top to bottom; look at that conv. Jaguar, you are driving, and you have a good job. Whenever anyone sees you, you're looking good. Now if she wanted to get married, Who's better than you? But that's not what she wants, and you were too damn dumb and blind to see that." The-Lou's Mom wiping the tears from her face. Will-Die said "It's like this momma. That kind of woman is just out for what she can get.

She knows that all these men out here want her, and all she does is used them. I bet if you can go back into her past, you find out about a whole lot of men; this woman has messed over. They probably end up alcoholics, on drugs, broke, or in the crazy house." Will-Die replied, as he knew Ny very well.

"You're right! The-Lou Mom said" Because I thought she was going to have your brother in that crazy house." Will-Die said.

"Naw! That will never happen to Luther! I taught him better than that. He had just never been in love before and didn't know how to act. But you know the signs now, don't you, little brother? You might fall in love again, but one thing you learned is if a woman lies to you. She can never in life be trusted. And Ny lies to you, and believe me, she will lie to you again. If she wants to come back, I'm going to tell you now that she is up to no good. Don't believe anything she says and watch what she does, and that will tell the whole story." Will-Die said. He was quite confident that The-Lou would not be trapped by Ny anymore, and he had finally moved on.

The-Lou Mom said. "I'm going to tell you something my mother told me a long time ago. If you lie, you will steal, and if you steal, one day, you will get yourself or somebody else killed. Remember that Luther!" The-Lou's mom said.

Cousin Nate said "Here is something I want you to think about, but I'm going to ask you a few questions first. Now you know, I used to be a heavy drug user. I saw Ny at the gas station, and she had lost a whole lot of weight. Don't get me wrong, she still looks good, but I want to know, when was the last time you were over at her house? The-Lou said, "yesterday."

"I remember the story you told me about how that dude was giving her his check about five months ago; now add another three months to that. Because the time she told you doesn't mean that's the time he started. So just assume that this guy has been giving Ny his check for eight months, and she is working and collecting child support. She should be doing pretty well. What I want to know is it's been about 4 months since the last time you were there. Does it look like she has anything new, like furniture or anything else, or does she still have the same shit over there from when I help you move her? The-Lou said,"The same things." Pay close attention, and I'm not saying that she is, but it sounds to me like she could be on drugs. You got three incomes, and you haven't improved on anything. Is her house junkie? The-Lou said, "Yes" Did she do anything outside to help the property value?" He continued.

"I work with my friend Jim sometimes, and we did put a deck on the back of the house about a week after she moved in," The-Lou replied.

"How does it look?" Nate asked The-Lou.

"She has a dog, and he's tearing it up. It looks like it's ten years old." The-Lou replied.

"These are some hard signs. The weight loss. No money? No new furniture? The house is junkie, and the dog is fucking up the deck.

Now you're not caring about your surrounding or your property. How did you end up getting back in there like that, with her anyway? Did she lose her job?" Nate said,

"She started calling, and one thing led to another. And she did mention that she was laid off." Bingo! Said Nate. Where is that dude she had living with her?" Nate continued.

"He left," The-Lou replied.

"Why?" Nate asked.

"She said, "God told him to go home." Then she said, "God told her the same thing. There was a pause, and they all looked at each other, then looked at The-Lou, then everybody burst out into laughter.

"That's bullshit! You know it, and all of us on this porch know it. What happened is that nigga lost his job, and she told his ass to go. Then blamed it on God. HA! HA!" Nate said, and he couldn't stop giggling.

"Tell me this, does she still have her car?" Nate questioned?

The-Lou said," No."

"What happened to it?" Nate asked; he was trying to show Ni's true colors to The-Lou so that he doesn't fall into her trap again.

"She told me that she turned it back in because the notes were too high," The-Lou replied.

"Ny told me she had that car for almost five years. Now you're going to turn it back in. Five years is about what they give you to pay for a car, and now you have to turn it back in. I hate to say this, but I'm almost convinced that girl is on drugs.

Give it a few years; I bet you will not even recognize her." Nate said.

A few days later, The-Lou is riding around with one of his cousins, Ray. He asks The-Lou if he is still messing around with Ny. The-Lou nods his head yes.

"Where does she work?" Ray asked.

"At the Water Company. But she is laid off now." The-Lou replied.

"My best friend works there. I am going to call him up and see what's up with her. How long had she been working there, cous? And her name is Nigeria Hines." Ray said.

"She's been there almost a year, and that's her name," The-Lou replied, looking at Ray. Ray pulls out his phone and dials a number.

"What up, Steve? This is your boy Ray. I'm riding with my cousin, and I'm going to put you on my speakerphone. Do you know a Nigeria Hines?" Ray said as soon as Steve received the call.

"Yes! Every man in here knows her, with that big fat round ass." Steve replied,

"What's going on with her?" Ray asked him.

"She is engaged to this dude name Ralph," Steve tells Ray The engagement part really catches The-Lou's attention. Several thoughts clumped his mind, and his heart started beating faster and faster with every passing minute.

"I don't know this for sure, but the word is that she is all about the money. We get an hour for lunch, and there is a cheap motel not far from the job. They say she has been seen coming out of there with a couple of brothers that work here and that they were paying her for that pussy. And I can believe that because if you see this dude Ralph. You know a woman like that ain't going to marry no nigga like him.

And you know he's paying. Ralph is just like another check that she doesn't have to work for." Steve continued.

"What does he do there? He might be some big-time manager." Ray said.

"Who, Ralph? Hell naw! He's on the bottom of the payroll. He is like a go for. Whatever they need him to do. Take out the trash, mop the floor, shit like that.

Well, now he ain't doing nothing now. Both of them got laid off. But look! I got to go. Hit me later." Steve yells and tells Ray everything about Ralph.

"My cousin Nate said that nigga probably lost his job, and Ny is laid off too.

That explains a little why she wants to come back. Now it all makes sense. I used to tell people that there was another man in Ni's life, but I just didn't know who it was.

Ny landed that job in August of last year. That is where she met Ralph, but she told me that she met him at church. So that's why she didn't buy me the shoes for my birthday or Christmas because she knew that she wasn't going to have me around too much longer anyway. She told me that she started seeing Ralph in April. I would see his car park outside of her house in March, but she had been seeing him ever since September of last year because she works with him, and that was around the time she started raising hell about any and everything. And wasn't none of that shit she was talking about my fault. What a lying bitch. I am supposed to see her tonight. "Don't you just hate a lying ass bitch?" Ray said. The-Lou was boiling with anger. How are tolerating a hoe like Ny Ray asked? Being madly in love with someone will make you do things you wouldn't ordinarily do. Besides we all make mistakes." The-Lou said. "Hey, cousin! Don't get we all make mistakes confused with flat out lies. Ray said. Your right! "I'm not going to be taking any shit off of her this time. The minute I think she is lying or doing things she shouldn't be doing. I'm going to bring it to her attention instead of ignoring it like I did before." The-Lou said. "It's going blow her mind when I tell her where she really knows Ralph from." The-Lou said.

When The-Lou saw Ny later that night, he wasted no time Confronting her about the engagement she has with Ralfh. Ny replied" He was depositing his whole check in my bank account and that is something you will never do. He let me use his car that I am driving right now to come over here to be with your ass. So stop with this bullshit. The-Lou said "I would deposit my money, plus give you everything I own if you would marry me. Ny said "Look here Luther, I have decided that I am not going to marry nobody. I told Ralph that our engagement is off". The-Lou said "So let me get this straight, you told him that and he still deposit his check in your account, still let you drive his car and you don't have sex with him. That's right! I get that unemployment check every week. The-Lou said" And you don't have sex with him. Ny said "I just told you. Stop asking me the same questions. Your the only one I am having sex with, now please drop it. Then Ny said "I will tell you this, I will spend some nights with him because I need his Car and you wont let me use any of yours. The-Lou said "Why should I. So you can use it to go over some other man house and fuck him! Like your using his car to come over here and fuck me. Like I said before, if you would marry me, I would give you everything that I own, but until that happens. You ain't using none of my cars, so keep on making a fool out of his dumb ass.

So The-Lou and Ny have an understanding, she would be with Ralfh a few day, then she would be with The-Lou a few days. When Ny wasn't around, The-Lou was seeing and having sex with other women but after a couple of weeks of this. The-Lou realize that these other women can't make him feel the way Ny does, so he stops seeing them and just look forward when its his turn to be with Ny. By this time The-Lou is more in love with Ny than ever. The-Lou was like a kid in a Candy store when it was his turn to see Ny. It was Sunny Sunday afternoon, The-Lou was feeling really good and was so happy because it is his turn to see Ny. Later that evening the weather changed to a serve thunder storm.

The-Lou lights went out in his house. He called Ny. The-Lou said. "Where are you at?" Ny answered.

"I'm with Ralph," Ny replied.

"What in the hell are you doing with him?" The-Lou asked her.

"I went over to his friend's house. I'm still with him, and I don't know when I will be coming back." She replied.

"You said that we were going to be together tonight. I need to spend the night with you because all of my electricity is out, and I don't have an alarm to wake me up in the morning." The-Lou said.

"Look! I will call you back in two hours." Ny said.

The-Lou hung up the phone and started calling other women who he could go spend the night with. The-Lou found 3 or 4 different women he could go spend the night with, but he wanted to be with Ny. Two hours later, Ny called.

"Hey! I don't know when I will be home. Ralph wants me to go somewhere else with him." Ny said. She wanted to cancel the plan The-Lou, all set to spend a night at her place. The-Lou said "It's getting late, and I need to go to sleep. Tell him to bring you home, and if he won't do it. Tell me where you are at, and I will come and get you." The-Lou said.

Ny hung up the phone on The-Lou. He is really mad now. The-Lou keeps calling until Ny answers the phone. Ny asked The-Lou did he want to talk to Ralph? The-Lou said, "Yes."

"Hello!" Ralph said. The-Lou said "So this must be Ralph because I don't have to tell you who you're talking to.

I'm going to ask you a question. Is Ny your woman?" The-Lou asked Ralph. He was quite pissed off, but he tried his best to control his voice and tone.

"No! But she said that you're not her man either." Ralph said.

Did she tell you that two weeks after you left, I have been fucking the shit out of her and spending the nights with her?" The-Lou told Ralph.

"No, she didn't. We agree that we were not going to have sex because of our religion." Ralph replied.

"Well, you held up your end of the barging because she has been over here giving me all of that pussy, and using your car to get over here, to bring it to me, she sure as hell didn't hold up her end of the barging." The-Lou scoffed and said.

"I'm going to have to talk to her about that," Ralph replied calmly. It looked as if it made no difference to him. The-Lou just couldn't believe his reaction. The-Lou is thinking to himself, this has to be the stupidest mother fucker that ever walk the face of the Earth of all time. This put a whole new meaning to the phase (THAT U CAN'T MAKE THIS SHIT UP)

"Put Ny back on the phone," The-Lou said to Ralph. Ny gets back on the phone, yelling and screaming at The-Lou.

"What you told him ain't going to change nothing! It's not going to change anything. He will still be here. What you said won't change anything!" Ny screamed her lungs out and was quite outrageous.

'Okay! So what? It won't change anything. Now is he ready to bring your ass home." The-Lou asked her sternly.

"I'm on my way home, but Ralph will not let me keep his car unless he can spend the night. And I have a job interview in the morning, so I have to use his car." Ny said".

The-Lou said "Get your ass out there and catch the mother fucking bus in the morning. I need to spend the night over there because my electricity is out." The-Lou said.

"Okay then! Both of you guys can spend the night." Ny replied.

"What! Have you lost your damn mind? What do you want? A threesome. I tell you what? I am on my way and his ass better not be there when I get there. Ny said" Don't come over here Luther! The-Lou said" I am on my way". The-Lou went and grab two of his guns A 357 and a Saturday Night Special. He running around the house waving his guns saying it's my turn, it's my turn. That Nigga ain't going to take my turn. What The-Lou Mom feared came to pass, The-Lou has went over the edge. The-Lou got behind the wheel of the car and before he pulled off, he heard something so loud that said" WHAT ARE YOU DOING? to this day, he didn't know if it was his conscience or did God actually speak to him. The-Lou thought about it, then another thought came to his mind. Do you remember when you went to The Penitentiary? The-Lou FLASHBACK!!

It was 1981 inside North County Boxing Jym, The Head coach came over to The-Lou and said to him, You have been training for 6 months and I think that your ready for your 1st fight. and we are going to Algoa. The-Lou was happy and he asked one of the guys where is Algoa and he said "Its a small town in Missouri. So the day of the fight, The-Lou and some other guys are shadow boxing and saying we are from The Big City, St. Louis Missouri. We are going to Algoa and beat the hell out of those Hillbillies, The-Lou and some of the other guys he box with are giving each other high fives and one of the guys said " Do yall know what Algoa is? The-Lou said "Hell yea! It's a small town in Missouri. The other Boxer said "Algoa ain't no small town in Missouri! The Lou said "Oh yea! Then what is it then brother" while he and the other guys are still shadow boxing, The other Boxer said " Algoa is a Penitentiary" When The-Lou and the other Boxers hear this, they came to a complete halt! The-Lou said "PENITENTIARY like in Jefferson City? The other Boxer said "Its in Jefferson City! Once that sunk in, one of the Boxers collapse and The-Lou kept saying to himself, what am i going to do? What am I going to do? Then The-Lou started thinking somebody say something, somebody say something and finally someone did. one of the boxers yelled out that he couldn't go, someone else asked 'Why" He said "I forgot, My Moma is moving today! That was The-Lou cue, then he yell out He is not lying because I am supposed to help and someone in background yell out "Me Too" The Head Boxing coach said if you guys don't get on this Bus, don't come back here to Box with us. So they all got on the Bus and 2 hours later when they arrived at Algoa, The-Lou never seen a fence that high with so much Razor Wire that it didn't even look real. As they where getting off the Bus, walking towards the gate, A Guard let them in and it look like at lease 8 to 900 Prisoners where in The Yard and some of them was walking right to them and one of them said "Where y'all from?" Someone yell out St. Louis, then some them said and it seem like at the same time they said "All of y'all are going to get knock the Hell out! Then the Prisoners was yelling and saying things that's hard to repeat, just believe whatever your thinking someone probably said it. The Prisoners was yelling so much that is became matter noise to The-Lou and the one thing The-Lou realize about his very 1st day inside A Penitentiary, that the Guards are not there to protect you, but there to make sure you don't leave because the Guard that let them in just disappeared and looking around, it seem like it was one guard for every 100 inmates, plus the Guards are not allowed to carry Guns for fear that the Inmates will over power then and take the Guns from them. One of the Boxers notice this and said "Man they don't even have any Guns on them! What if they wanted to riot? What would we do? The-Lou said like it or not, we are in here now and we got to Jail as if we were locked up ourselves and to make bad matters worse, we had no idea where to go because it was the Head coach 1st time going there also. So the group of Boxers, we all just standing there listening to the Prisoners insults, then The-Lou's sparing partner Hawk turned around and said "we are fighters! Lets come in here and do what we came to do. So all of us fallowed his lead when he started walking, so we all started walking, the only problem was that neither he or head coach didn't know were they was going. So as we are walking and the Prisoners as our tour guides, they are in front of us, on the left side of us, on the right side of us, they are behind us as we are walking and they are constantly yelling insults, then The Little Black Missile just couldn't take it anymore and he step from the crown and pointed up to the Sky and said "Fuck all of y'all! I will Kick everyone ass in here, I am a Pro Boxer, I am 2 and 0, The Head Coach grabbed him and said, look these men are already wound up, let's not give them more energy and for a few seconds it seem like they all got a quite, I don't think they could believe he said that themselves, then they went back to harassing us. We finally found the Auditorium and as we were walking up the steps, the Prisoners was on each side of us, some of them tried to Sucker punch some of us and when we finally reach the top and stepped inside, it seem like to The-Lou that it was more prisoners inside than there was in the Yard. As The-Lou was walking a Prisoner that look to be in his mid 30'S asked him he said" Hey little brother! The-Lou said ' What's up man? The Prisoner said "Is the Arch still there? The-Lou couldn't believe what he just heard, because no one have ever asked him that question before and haven't asked that question to this very day. The-Lou just nodded his head yes and kept walking. One of The-Lou sparing partners said ' Luther! Did you hear what he asked you? The-Lou still in shock of what he just heard. The sparing partner ask the-Lou again. Luther! Luther! Did you hear what he asked you? Then The-Lou yelled out I heard him! The sparing partner said "As long as I have been living, The Arch has always been there, how long has he been in here? The-Lou says how old are you, His sparing partner says I am 16. The-Lou says well let's start there. The Arch was completed in 1966, it's 1981 and that dude looks like he is in his mid 30"s, What if he got locked up at 16, that mean he could have been in hear since 1964 or 1965 so the reason he is asking is probably because he never seen it! Then The-Lou gets weight in and at the time he was 125 lbs and the guy he was suppose to fight had to pull out, so when The-Lou got into the ring and when he look over at the other corner, there was a dude standing there that look like he was 6'2" and The-Lou says to his coach "I would like to see that dude on the scale because ain't no way he weighs 125 pounds, The head Coach said, you can take him, this is what we trained you for, that why we would have you box guys twice your size. The-Lou said "This can't be real, this shit only happens in the movies. The Bell rung and The-Lou charged him throwing punches, the inmate hit The-Lou and pushed him down. The-Lou is looking up at The Ref like are you going to wave that off, but instead The Ref was calling it a Knockdown, The-Lou said to himself, "Well I am in The Penitentiary" So The-Lou got back up and for 3 rounds they was fighting, Then The-Lou hit him with a solid shot to the Chin, The Inmate fell back on the rope and The-Lou kept punching upward with the one-two combo for about 10 punches straight, the Inmate look like he was ready to go and then the Bell rung ending the fight! The MC said that we have a split decision, The Prisoners started getting loud, The-Lou could see the Judges had a worry look on their faces and it was announced that the Inmate won the fight! As The-Lou step out of the ring, some of the Inmates came up to him and said You kick his big ass, they took that fight from you, The-Lou thank them and The-Lou couldn't help thinking that if that fight was somewhere else, The Judges may have given it to him. The-Lou believe he lost that fight because the Inmate had home Penitentiary advantage.

The-Lou is changing out of his boxing shorts and shirt into his clothes. He walks into the Auditorium to watch the remaining boxing matches, he see's some guys he knows, one of them name D-Jack and he walk up to The-Lou and said "What's up Luther? I didn't know you can box. I know when y'all walk in here a lot of the inmates was giving y'all a hard time but in reality, majority of us have a lot of respect for anyone have the courage to come in here and fight, with very little protection because the guards ain't going to do shit to help you. The-Lou said. "That's the first thing I notice. The guard let us inside, locked the gate and went on a coffee break. I think it was the inmates that showed us how to get to the auditorium. D-Jack said "I don't know how true this is but some of the shot callers said don't fuck with y'all too much. The-Lou gave him a look, then said "well I guess they didn't listen to them because those inmates was letting us have it. D-Jack said "that ain't shit, they was just running their mouths. But let me tell you this, I do admire y'all courage, but coming in here with all of these dangerous men with little to no protection was truly insane. Anything can pop off at any time. You know some guys in here got 20 or 30 years and it's a few that have life, waiting to go behind The Wall so they truly don't give a fuck. Some guys are scared to fight so they pay for protection, one dude just got beat up real bad because he was new and he was looking inside another inmates cell and just like someone looking inside your house. I have a knife on me and I have some bury in the yard for my added protection. You have guys that will try steal from you and if you let them get away with it, then everyone think they can take your shit. We have zoom zoom and wham whams. The-Lou said boom boom and bam bam, what kind of Flintstone shit y'all going on up in here? K-Jack laughs a little and he said "it's zoom zoom and wham whams. They are snacks and some of these inmates will beat the hell out of you for them, if they are lifer's, you could lose your life over them. A honey bun on the streets is about 15 cents, Roman Noodles are 5 cents, you could lose your life over that because the food in here is fucked up. Please don't get seriously get sick in here because if you do, you should go pick out your coffin because the quack nurses and doctors they have on staff came from the school of Dr. Suess and you have to watch out for some of these Booty Bandits because if any of them step to me, I am going to stick them and keep it moving. D-Jack raised up his shirt and showed The-Lou his home-made knife. Remember as long as your in here never relax. It's 1500 inmates and I see 6 guards with no guns and it's 20 of y'all. What could y'all do if they wanted to pop things off? There would be nothing y'all could do. So prey on your way out of here. All of the boxing matches are over and it's time to leave. D-Jack shakes The-Lou's hand then said "I hope the next time I see you, I will be on the outside and not you in here on the inside. The -Lou said "I had plans on selling weed with a brother I know from The Vaughan Projects, but after being in here. If I can't get my money the right way, then I won't get no money at all. Trush me. I will never step foot in another Penitentiary for as long as I live. D-Jack said "One other thing I want to say, I was taking to some of the other inmates and we all agreed. They stole that fight from you Luther. You should have won". D-Jack shakes The-Lou's hand then they parted ways. The-Lou is secretly praying to God that they can make it out of there with no problems. It was on The-Lou's mind what D-Jack said about it could pop off and it's 1500 of them 20 of us with hardly no protection. As The-Lou was leaving he overheard 2 inmates arguing. The 1st inmate said "If I can't live like a man, I can die like one. The 2nd inmate said fuck you! I can die or we all can die! That really got The-Lou's attention and now he see's a small fight at the exit he is supposed to walk out of, now the words D-Jack said to him really got The-Lou paranoid. The-Lou starts thinking, what if turns into a full scale riot, they take us hostage, then the inmates look like they broke up on their own because it look like the guards wasn't doing much to stop it. The-Lou got on the other side of that gate it was like a ton of bricks lifted off of his shoulders. The-Lou got on the Bus and found out that the scuffle was about some of the inmates where trying to snatch the trophy from some of other inmates. After The-Lou **flashback** on that. He got out of the Car and went back into the house and put his Guns up.

Then he grab a bottle, a fifth of Hennessy and fix himself a drink, he turn on the cd player and it was just playing random songs, the first song came on was by the Temptations, it started off saying "Sunshine blue skies please go away, my girl has found another and she has gone away, with her went my future, my life is filled with gloom, so day after day I will stay locked up in my room. I know to you it may sound strange but I wish it would rain. The-Lou have heard this song so many times but this time he is really feeling what they are singing about. The-Lou can't take it any more so he changes the cd to another random song and this one was by The Main Ingredients and this song started off saying "Ok so your heart is broke, you sit around whining and crying, you say you even thinking about dying, so did this, everybody plays the fool. The-Lou really didn't want to hear that song then he changes it again, this time Smokey Robinson came on The-Lou listen to it and then this verse really caught his attention" Just like the desert shows a thirsty man green oasis when there is only sand, she lured me into something I should have dodge because the love I saw in you was just a mirage. That really him home with The-Lou because that is how he feels about Ny.

❧

A few days later Paula calls The-Lou. Paula said "I heard you talk to Ralfh? Now he doesn't want Ny using his car anymore after what you told him about her coming over your house with his car. The-Lou said "I am totally done with her, if it wasn't for God, I would have done something I would have regrated for the rest of my life. As far as Ny goes. I rather be with a woman that looks like a dog and treats me like the man that I am; before, I would be with the finest woman in the world, and she treats me like a dog. My name is not Milton Bradley, and I'm not one of the Parker Brothers. Let Ny play her games with somebody else." The-Lou said.

"Well, she said that she needs a friend, and you won't deal with her. She ran into Motubu, and you know she doesn't have a car, and he offered her to use his."

The-Lou said " That is just what I'm talking about; she said she would never have anything else to do with him because he is crazy. Now she over there fucking him too." The-Lou scoffed and replied.

"No, she's not! Ny says that they are just friends, and he wants to help her out.

Besides, she says you're the only one she really misses in bed." Paula said, trying to clear the mess between them.

"Let me tell you something, Paula! Number 1, ain't no man is going to offer his car to a woman and let her drive it if he is not going to bed with her. Except Ralph and I still can't believe that shit! Especially if it's someone he had a relationship with and still has feeling for. The second thing is If Ny felt that way about me in the bedroom. She would have treated me a whole lot better than what she did. That woman doesn't give a good fuck about me and nobody else. The only person she loves is herself and what's hers. That is it. when it comes to Ny. So the next time we talk, don't bring her damn name up. Hey! I got this woman waiting on me. I got to go! Later." The-Lou said. He made it quite clear to Paula that he is not even least interested in Ny or any of her lies. The-Lou move on from Ny and start a new chapter in his life.

XVII

⚘ Inside Ny's House

*R*alph and Ny are yelling at each other.

"Who is this African dude that is calling the house?" Ralph asked NY.

"Don't you worry about it? I got the house phone back on, and it's my house.

And if you don't like it? You can leave now, but if you got to know? He is a friend from a long time ago. You just be happy that Luther is not calling, and if you keep acting up. I will sell this house and move in with him, and you will never see me again. Remember! He wants me at all costs, just like you do. He calls Paula all the time, telling her how badly he wants me back. So either you're going to deal with it or not." Ny replies.

"As much as I have been helping you. Letting you use my car and giving you my whole check. Especially after what Luther told me, Yes I didn't let you use the car after that but I forgive you and now I'm letting you use the car again and I would like a little more respect than that." Ralph yelled at her.

❧ Outside Of Ny's House

Jr is being dropped off by some of his friends, and Motubu is pulling up at the same time. Motubu has been coming over from time to time to see Ny whenever she gets rid of Ralph by dropping him off at his cousin's house and keeping the car. So Jr didn't think twice about Ralph being in the house when he saw Motubu pull up. Jr and Motubu spoke to each other, then Jr opened the door and let Motubu in. Ny comes out of her bedroom, and Ralph is right behind her. They both look up, and there is Motubu standing there in the hallway.

"Who in the fuck is this?" Ralph said, pointing out to Mobutu.

Ny is shocked, not only to see Motubu standing there but to hear Ralph curse for the first time. Jr is getting a little afraid of what he thinks is getting ready to happen because he knows that Motubu will act crazy.

"Who in the hell are you? Ny used to be my woman, and we are going to get back together. I have been letting her use my car and giving her money to pay her bills. Now why don't you leave so I can talk to her?" Mobutu said in a fit of rage.

"So this is the African friend of yours." Ralph turned to Ny and said. He heard the accent and recognized that he was African.

"This is my damn woman. I let her use my car, and I'm helping her pay the bills too. So you get the fuck out of here." He continued yelling at Mobutu.

"If you want me out! You better put me out." Mobutu said. He was now getting out of control.

Motubu walks up to Ralph and punches him in the face. Then they started fighting. Motubu was getting the better of Ralph. Jr and Ny were able to hold Motubu just long enough for Ralph to get away. Ralph ran out the front door, and Motubu started laughing, talking about what a punk he was. HA! HA!

"Who told you to come over here unannounced?" Ny yelled at Mobutu.

"Why not? You come over to my house unannounced." Mobutu said.

Right, then Ralph comes back into the house, yelling and cursing, with a gun in his hand. Ny can't believe that Ralph would act like this. Motubu is standing in front of Jr. Ralph points the gun at Motubu and yells out," I'm going to kill your ass nigga" Then Ralph pulls the trigger, and Motubu drives to the floor, and the bullet hits Jr. For a few seconds, everyone stands motionless. When Ralph sees that he shot Jr instead of Motubu, he drops the gun and starts crying.

As soon as Motubu saw Ralph drop the gun, he got up off the floor and ran out of the house. Then jumped into his car and then pulled off. Ny is losing her mind because Jr is lying there unconscious, and he's starting to bleed badly. Ny is holding Jr and begging God not to take her son. Ralph grabs the phone and calls 911. The ambulance came and took Jr to the hospital. Ny called her parents and Nick and told them what happened. Mr. and Mrs. Baker ran right out of the house to the airport with what they had on and didn't worry about packing any bags.

 ❦ Inside The Hospital-Waiting Room-

4 Hours Later Ny, Nick, Paula, and Mr. and Mrs. Baker are in the waiting room. Mr. and Mrs. Baker had arrived about 30 minutes ago. When they reached the airport, a flight was boarding from New York to St. Louis, and it had some seats left.

"Oh, God! Please don't take my son away from me." Ny prayed to God and couldn't control her tears. The fear of losing her son was taking her life away.

Ny just kept saying that prayer. Mrs. Baker grabs Ny and starts talking to her.

Ny stops crying and starts listening.

"I just finished talking to your boyfriend before the Police took him to jail for unlawful use of a weapon. Whatever happens, if Jr pulls thru this or not. Don't try to send that man to jail for something you brought to your home. He told me what happened and how you had been going back and forth with some other guy that you we're seeing. Then he said he didn't know where this guy came from. One day this man starts calling, and the next thing he knows, he shows up at your house and starts beating him up." Mrs. Baker said.

"Ny! Please listen to me, baby! You can't keep on taking money from these guys if you don't like them that way. Don't you know that is another form of stealing?

This man said that he was giving you his whole check and letting you use his car, and he came to find out that you were doing the same thing with this other guy. Now look where it has gotten you. Was it worth it, Ny? You know the old saying. If you will lie? And you have been doing that your whole life. If you lie, you will steal! I know about what you did to that man Don back in New York. Your brother had gotten drunk one day, and they started talking about it, and I overheard them in the other room, so I made them tell me the whole story. I couldn't believe that you would do something like that, and all that man tried to do was help you?" She continued.

"Well! He was getting my body!" Ny replied.

"And according to your ex-husband, so was everybody else; that's one good reason why you and Nick are not married right now! And if you and Nick were still married, there would be a damn good chance we wouldn't be sitting up in this hospital waiting on whether or not Jr is going to live or die. And this is what brings me to my conclusion. If you lie, you will steal, and if you steal, you can put yourself or somebody else in a place where they can be killed. So far, that hasn't happened yet because your son is still alive." Mrs. Baker said. Before she could add more, Mr.

Baker interrupted the conversation and said. "Oh yes, it has. Ny has gotten somebody killed."

"Who?" Mrs. Baker asked in surprise.

"Do you all remember Lorenzo?" Mr. Baker asked his wife.

"That's a blast from the past," Ny said, wiping tears from her eyes.

"Yes! I remember him. The last I heard was that he was missing, and did he ever turn up? (Mrs. Baker thinks about it, then puts her hands over her face, then starts shaking her head) Joe, please tell me you didn't?" Mrs. Baker said.

"Yes, I did! That 25-year-old punk had no business messing around with my 16-year-old daughter and getting her pregnant. So I made sure he wasn't going to do it to anybody else. I shot him, then ran him threw a grinder and then mixed up his remains with concrete, and buried him in a hole 6 feet deep 2 hours outside of New York City on a farm. That was over 25 years ago, and I never talked about it until now." Mr. Baker confessed that he had killed Lorenzo for what he did to Ny.

"Well, I was wrong. Ny, you have lied, Ny, you steal, and now what breaks my heart is that now I know that you have gotten somebody killed. And it all started with lies. When is it going to stop? Will it take your son's life to make you understand the things that you are doing are not right?" Mrs. Baker asked her. She was quite scared of the fact that her son might have to pay for all her sins.

Ny starts crying again and begging the Lord to save her child. The doctor is looking for the Hines family. When he finds them, he takes them into a private room.

"Is the mother and father present (Ny and Nick both say yes)? I am sorry to tell you that your son didn't make it. We did all that we could, but he lost too much blood. I'm sorry." The doctor asked as he stepped out of the OT.

Ny yelled out a loud scream and started crying and going hysterical. It took everybody in the room to restrain her.

"I'm sorry, God! I'm sorry, God! Please bring my son back to me. I won't use lies and use people no more, God! Please bring my son back to me." Ny said, screaming and begging God for forgiveness, but it was already too late for that.

A minute later, the doctor who had just left came walking back into the room.

"Please, may I have your attention for a minute? I was given the wrong information. This is the Hines family, right? (Everybody said yes)

"Okay! Your son is going to be all right. It was another family that came at the same time you all did, and their son had been shot too. And their last name was Hunts. So, the staff got the names confused, you know, with the Hines, Hunts ketchup anybody can make that mistake, right!"

The Dr. said, laughing. The entire family stood there in disbelief; it was like a miracle for Ny and Nick as God had saved her son's life.

"I can laugh about this with you all because your son is going to be all right, and you can take him home in the morning. We'll keep him overnight just to make sure everything is all right. Now! My biggest problem is that I told the Hunts family first that their son was going to be all right. How do I go over there and tell them we made a mistake with the identification, and their son didn't make it? Well, I guess that's why I make big bucks. I'm happy for you all. Goodbye." The doctor continued and went away.

After hearing the news, Ni's tears went from pain to Joy. Ny is on her knees, thanking God.

"The Lord has given you a chance. I hope you get your life together. And please find a man that you want and love and stay with him." Mrs. Baker said and advised Ny to mend her ways now!

"She could have this one back if she thinks she learned a lesson," Nick said as he thanked God for saving his son's life.

"This is almost too good to be true! I have my son back, and I can have back the one man I truly did love. I promise that I have learned, and I will be with you until the day we die, and I will be the best wife any man could hope for." Ny replied she was really thankful for what had happened and that God had saved her son.

"I believe you, Ny, and just like Al Green said, let's get married today," Nick asked Ny holding her hand.

Everybody is happy. Ny and Nick were married a few weeks later. Nick helped Ny get her job back at Leu Motors, and with her degree, she ended up becoming his boss. Ny and Nick bought a house bigger than the one they had before, and Ny never lied again, and they lived a happy and great life together. The-Lou is back to chasing the women. Motubu has never gone over to another women's house again unannounced, and Ralph was spreading the word in jail for two years upend his release. He now has a big church, a great family, a woman who truly loves him, and a really good living.